A Christmas Carol *Christmas Book*

A
Chris
Carol

Christmas Book

tmas

Tim Hallinan, Text

David James, Photography

Rudolph de Harak & Associates, Inc.
Book Design

Entertainment Partners, Inc.
Producers of "A Christmas Carol"
Television Special

Printed in the United States of America

Table of Contents

Preface

Charles Dickens was the poet laureate of Christmas, and *A Christmas Carol* was his greatest tribute to this joyous season. Ebenezer Scrooge, Bob Cratchit and Tiny Tim are known all over the world, wherever the holiday is celebrated. Dickens helped to create, with a kind of seasonal nostalgia, the Christmas of roaring fires, hot punch, and "God Rest Ye Merry, Gentlemen."

As English as the Dickens Christmas was, it has transcended the time and place in which it was created and has become universal. Part of its appeal lies in the values Dickens celebrated, values that appeal to people everywhere. For Dickens, the holiday season was a time to fulfill our obligations toward those less fortunate than ourselves. The real cheer of the holiday, he suggests, comes from doing our part to help ensure peace on earth, good will to men.

This book is a celebration of the Dickens Christmas, brightened by pictures from Dickens' own time and by photographs from IBM's television presentation of *A Christmas Carol.* It is a cornucopia of ideas, information and projects to enliven the holiday season, based on the best-loved Christmas story ever written.

Whether you use "A Christmas Carol *Christmas Book*" as a resource for holiday ideas, an introduction to the Dickens Christmas, or simply a book to be read and shared for pleasure, we at IBM hope it enhances your enjoyment of this festive holiday season.

The photographs in the first section of this book were taken in Shrewsbury, England, during the filming of *A Christmas Carol.* This major retelling of the Charles Dickens classic stars George C. Scott as Ebenezer Scrooge. It is the first adaptation to be filmed in color entirely on location, and the most faithful to Dickens' classic tale.

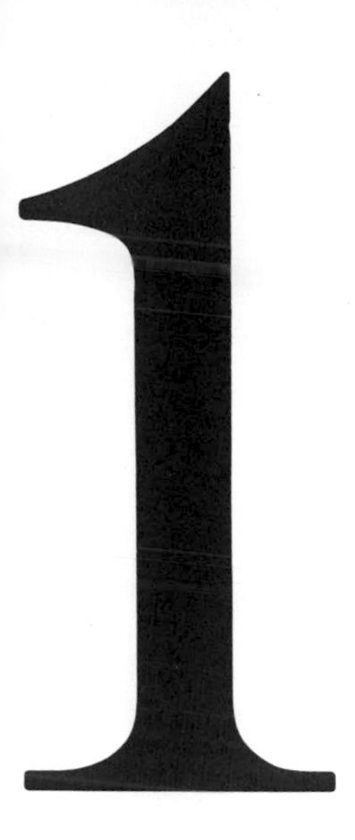

A Christmas Carol: A Story in Pictures

George C. Scott	*Ebenezer Scrooge*
Frank Finlay	*Jacob Marley*
Angela Pleasence	*Ghost of Christmas Past*
Edward Woodward	*Ghost of Christmas Present*
Michael Carter	*Ghost of Christmas Yet to Come*
David Warner	*Bob Cratchit*
Susannah York	*Mrs. Cratchit*
Anthony Walters	*Tiny Tim*
Roger Rees	*Fred Holywell*
Caroline Langrishe	*Janet Holywell*
Lucy Gutteridge	*Belle*
Nigel Davenport	*Silas Scrooge*
Mark Strickson	*Young Scrooge*
Joanne Whalley	*Fan*
Timothy Bateson	*Mr. Fezziwig*
Michael Gough	*Mr. Poole*
John Quarmby	*Mr. Hacking*
Peter Woodthorpe	*Old Joe*
Liz Smith	*Mrs. Dilber*

Marley was dead, to begin with. There is no doubt whatever about that. Old Marley was dead as a doornail.

Marley's Ghost

Scrooge never painted out old Marley's name. The firm was known as Scrooge and Marley. Sometimes people new to the business called Scrooge Scrooge, and sometimes Marley, but he answered to both names. It was all the same to him.

Oh, but he was a tightfisted hand at the grindstone, Scrooge! He was a squeezing, wrenching, grasping, clutching, covetous old sinner! Hard and sharp as flint. The cold within him froze his old features, nipped his pointed nose, stiffened his gait, made his eyes red, his thin lips blue, and spoke out shrewdly in his grating voice.

Once upon a time–of all the good old days in the year, on Christmas Eve–old Scrooge sat busy in his countinghouse, keeping his eye upon his clerk, who was copying letters. Scrooge had a very small fire, but the clerk's fire looked like one coal.

"A Merry Christmas, uncle!" cried a cheerful voice. It was the voice of Scrooge's nephew, Fred.

"Bah!" said Scrooge. "Humbug!"

"Christmas a humbug, uncle? Don't be cross!"

"What else can I be, when I live in such a world of fools as this? What's Christmastime to you but a time for paying bills without money, a time for finding yourself a year older but not an hour richer? If I could work my will, every idiot who goes about with 'Merry Christmas' on his lips would be boiled in his own pudding and buried with a stake of holly through his heart."

"Don't be angry, uncle. Come! Dine with us tomorrow."

"Good afternoon," said Scrooge. His nephew left the room without an angry word. He stopped at the outer door to bestow the greetings of the season on the clerk.

At length, the hour of shutting up the countinghouse arrived. "You'll want all day tomorrow, I suppose?" said Scrooge to his clerk.

"If quite convenient, sir."

"It's not convenient," said Scrooge, "and it's not fair. If I was to stop your wages for it, I imagine you'd think yourself ill-used, wouldn't you?"

The clerk observed that it was only once a year.

"A poor excuse for picking a man's pocket every 25th of December, but I suppose you must have the whole day. Be here all the earlier next morning."

The clerk promised that he would, and Scrooge walked out with a growl.

"And a Merry Christmas to you, Mr. Scrooge," the clerk called cheerfully after him.

Scrooge strode quickly through the streets of London, ignoring the crowds of happy people, turning a deaf ear to the songs of the carolers. He had business to transact. At the Exchange, he climbed the stairs and stalked into the great hall.

After charging a great deal more for a quantity of corn than it was worth, and feeling very pleased with himself about it, Scrooge was accosted by two pleasant-looking gentlemen.

"Mr. Scrooge, I presume," began one of the gentlemen.

"Yes, sir," muttered Scrooge, "you do."

"At this festive season of the year, Mr. Scrooge, a few of us are endeavoring to raise a fund to buy the poor some meat and drink and means of warmth."

"Are there no prisons?" asked Scrooge. "And the workhouses? Are they still in operation?"

"Many can't go there. And many would rather die."

"If they would rather die, they had better do it, and decrease the surplus population. Good afternoon, gentlemen."

Scrooge lived in chambers which had once belonged to his partner, Marley. The yard was so dark that even Scrooge, who knew its every stone, groped about with his hands for the doorknocker, which was very large.
Now, let it be borne in mind that Scrooge had not wasted a single thought on Marley in quite some time. And then let any man explain how it happened that Scrooge, having his key in the lock of the door, saw not a knocker, but Marley's face.

Marley's face, with ghostly spectacles turned up on his ghostly forehead. The hair was curiously stirred, as if by breath or hot air, and, though the eyes were wide open, they were perfectly motionless.

As Scrooge looked fixedly at this phenomenon, it was a knocker again. He put his hand upon the key again, turned it steadily, walked in, and lighted his candle. He fastened the door, and walked across the hall and up the broad echoing stairs, without a thought for the darkness. Darkness was cheap, and Scrooge liked it.

Sitting room, bedroom, storeroom—all as they should be. Quite satisfied, he closed his door and locked himself in. Then, secured against surprise, he put on his dressing gown and slippers and sat down before the fire to eat his porridge.

Suddenly the cellar door flew open with a booming sound, and then he heard the noise much louder, on the floor below; then coming up the stairs; then coming straight toward his room.

"It's humbug still," said Scrooge. "I won't believe it."

Without a pause, it came on through the heavy door and passed into the room before his eyes. Upon its coming in, the dying fire leaped up, as though it cried, "I know him! Marley's Ghost!" And indeed it was.

The same face, the very same. Marley in his pigtail, usual waistcoat, tights and boots. The chain he drew was clasped around his middle. It was long and wrapped around him, and it was made of cashboxes, keys, padlocks, deeds and heavy purses, all made of steel. A folded kerchief was bound about his head and chin.

"What do you want with me?" said Scrooge, coldly.
"Much!"–Marley's voice, no doubt about it.
"Who are you?"
"In life, I was your partner, Jacob Marley."
"Humbug, I tell you. Humbug!"

At this the spirit raised a frightful cry and shook his chain; and when he took off the bandage round his head, his lower jaw dropped down upon his chest. Scrooge fell upon his knees and clasped his hands before his face.
"Mercy! Dreadful apparition, why do you trouble me?"
"It is required of every man," the Ghost said, "that the spirit within him should walk among his fellow men, and travel far and wide; and if that spirit goes not forth in life, it is condemned to do so after death. In life, my spirit never roved beyond the confines of our dreary countinghouse, and now weary journeys lie before me."
"But you were always a good man of business, Jacob," faltered Scrooge.
"Business!" cried the Ghost. "Mankind was my business. The common welfare was my business; charity, mercy, forbearance and benevolence were, all, my business. The dealings of my trade were but a drop of water in the comprehensive ocean of my business!"

Scrooge was very much dismayed to hear the specter going on at this rate, and began to shake with fear.

"I am here tonight to warn you that you have yet a chance of escaping my fate."

"You were always a good friend to me," said Scrooge. "Thank you!"

"You will be haunted," resumed the Ghost, "by Three Spirits."

"I–I think I'd rather not," said Scrooge.

"Expect the first tonight, when the bell tolls one. Expect the second on the stroke of two. The third shall appear in its own good time."

When he had said these words, the apparition walked backward from Scrooge; and at every step he took, the window raised itself a little, so that when the specter reached it, it was wide open, and he floated out upon the bleak, dark night.

Scrooge closed the window. He tried to say "Humbug!" but stopped at the first syllable. He went straight to bed, without undressing, and fell asleep immediately.

The First Spirit

When Scrooge awoke, he heard the chimes of a neighboring clock striking the four quarters.

"The hour itself," said Scrooge triumphantly, "and nothing else!" But he had spoken too soon, and now the clock struck the hour, with a deep, dull, hollow, melancholy *one*.

Light flashed up in the room upon the instant; the curtains of his bed were drawn aside, and Scrooge found himself face to face with an unearthly visitor.

It was a strange figure–like a child. It wore a tunic of the purest white, and round its waist was bound a lustrous belt. But the strangest thing about it was a bright, clear jet of light that sprung from the crown of its head.

"Who, and what, are you?" Scrooge demanded.
"I am the Ghost of Christmas Past."
"Long past?"
"No. Your past." It put out its hand as it spoke, and clasped him gently by the arm. "Rise, and walk with me!"

Even as the words were spoken, they stood upon an open country road. The city had entirely vanished.

"Good Heavens!" said Scrooge. "I was bred in this place. I was a boy here."

They left the high road and soon approached a mansion of dull red brick. "The school is not quite deserted," said the Ghost. "A solitary child, neglected by his friends, is left there still."

A lonely boy was reading near a feeble fire, and Scrooge sat down to see his poor forgotten self as he used to be.

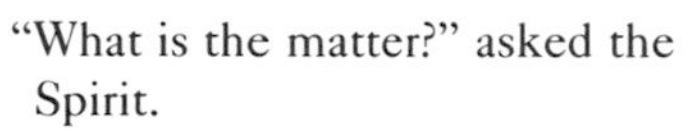

"What is the matter?" asked the Spirit.

"Nothing, nothing. There was a boy singing a Christmas carol at my door last night. I should like to have given him something. That's all."

The Ghost smiled thoughtfully and waved its hand, saying as it did so, "Let us see another Christmas."

Scrooge's former self grew a little larger at the words. The door opened, and a girl, younger than the boy, came darting in. "I have come to bring you home, dear brother! Home, for good and all. Father is so much kinder than he used to be, and we're to be together all the Christmas long, and have the merriest time in all the world."

"Always a delicate creature," said the Ghost. "She died a young woman, and had, as I think, children."

"One child," Scrooge returned.

"True. Your nephew!"

Scrooge seemed uneasy in his mind, and answered briefly, "Yes."

Although they had but that moment left the school behind them, the Ghost stopped at a certain warehouse door. They went in.
"Why, it's old Fezziwig!" cried Scrooge. "Bless his heart, it's Fezziwig alive again!"

Scrooge's former self, now a grown young man, came briskly in, accompanied by his fellow apprentice.
"Yo ho, Dick! Ebenezer!" said Fezziwig. "Clear everything away, my lads, and let's have lots of room here!"
Clear away! It was done in a minute. And in came a fiddler. In came Mrs. Fezziwig. In came the three young Miss Fezziwigs. In came all the young men and women employed in the business.

There were dances, and more dances, and there was cake, and there was a great piece of cold roast. And then there were still more dances.
When the clock struck eleven, this domestic ball ended.

"A small matter," said the Ghost, "to make these silly folks so full of gratitude. Fezziwig has spent but a few pounds of your mortal money."

"It isn't that, Spirit. The happiness he gives is as great as if it had cost a fortune." Scrooge felt the Spirit's glance and stopped.

"What is the matter?" asked the Ghost.

"Nothing particular. It's just... for a moment I thought of my clerk... of Bob Cratchit... it's nothing."

"My time grows short," observed the Spirit. "Quick!"

Again Scrooge saw himself. He was older now, a man in the prime of life. He was not alone, but sat by the side of a fair young girl in whose eyes there were tears.

"It is Belle," whispered Scrooge.

"It matters little to you," she said. "Another idol has displaced me."

"What idol?" rejoined the younger Scrooge.

"A golden one. I have seen your nobler aspirations fall off, one by one, until the master-passion, profit, engrosses you."

"Even if I have grown wiser, what then?" he retorted. "I am not changed toward you."

She shook her head. "Our contract is an old one. It was made when we were both poor and content to remain so."

"Have I ever sought release?"

"In words, never. But if you were free today, can I believe that you would choose a poor girl? No. I release you, with a full heart for the love of him you once were. May you be happy in the life you have chosen!"

They parted.

"Spirit!" cried Scrooge. "Show me no more! Conduct me home. Why do you delight to torture me?"

"I told you these were shadows of the things that have been. That they are what they are, do not blame me."

"Remove me! I cannot bear it!"

Scrooge observed that the Spirit's light was burning high and bright. In sudden anger, he seized its cap and pressed it down over its head. Scrooge was conscious of being exhausted and of being in his own bedroom. He had barely time to reel to bed before he sank into a heavy sleep.

The Second Spirit

Awakening in the middle of a prodigiously tough snore, Scrooge had no occasion to be told that the bell was upon the stroke of two. Five minutes, ten minutes, a quarter of an hour went by, yet nothing came. All this time, he lay upon his bed, the very core and center of a blaze of ruddy light which streamed upon it. At last, he began to think that the source of this ghostly light might be the adjoining room. He got up softly and shuffled in his slippers to the door.

The moment Scrooge's hand was upon the lock, a strange voice called him by name and bade him enter. He obeyed.

It was his own room. But it had undergone a surprising transformation. Crisp leaves of holly, mistletoe and ivy reflected back the light, as if so many little mirrors had been scattered there; and heaped on the floor, to form a kind of throne, were turkeys, geese, great joints of meat, chestnuts, cherry-cheeked apples, juicy oranges and seething bowls of punch. In easy state upon this couch there sat a jolly giant, glorious to see.

"I am the Ghost of Christmas Present," said the Spirit. "Look upon me."

It was clothed in one simple green robe, bordered with white fur. Its brown curls were long and free.

"Spirit," said Scrooge submissively, "conduct me where you will. Tonight, if you have anything to teach me, let me profit by it."

"Touch my robe!"

Scrooge did as he was told, and held it fast.

Holly, mistletoe, berries, meat, oysters, pies, puddings and punch all vanished instantly, and Scrooge and the Spirit stood in the city street on Christmas morning. There was nothing very cheerful in the climate, and yet there was an air of cheerfulness everywhere that the brightest summer sun might have endeavored to diffuse in vain.

It was a remarkable quality of the Ghost that, notwithstanding its gigantic size, it could accommodate itself to any place with ease; and perhaps it was its pleasure in showing off this power that led it straight to the small dwelling of Scrooge's clerk, Bob Cratchit. Mrs. Cratchit was busily setting the Christmas table, assisted by Miss Belinda Cratchit, while Master Peter Cratchit plunged a fork into the saucepan of potatoes. And now two smaller Cratchits came bursting in and danced about the table.
And in came Bob, the father, with Tiny Tim upon his shoulder.

Alas for Tiny Tim, he bore a little crutch, and had his limbs supported by an iron frame!
"And how did little Tim behave in church?" asked Mrs. Cratchit.
"As good as gold," said Bob, "and better." His voice was tremulous when he told them this, and trembled more when he said that Tiny Tim was growing strong and hearty.
Now Master Peter and the two young Cratchits went to fetch the goose, with which they soon returned in high procession.
There never was such a goose! Bob said he didn't believe there ever was such a goose cooked; indeed, as Mrs. Cratchit said with great delight, they hadn't eaten it all. But now Mrs. Cratchit left the room alone to bring the pudding in.

Oh, a wonderful pudding! Bob Cratchit said that he regarded it as the greatest success achieved by Mrs. Cratchit since their marriage. Everybody had something to say about it, but nobody said, or thought, it was at all a small pudding for a large family.

At last the dinner was all done, and the Cratchit family drew round the hearth, and Bob proposed:

"A Merry Christmas to us all, my dears. God bless us."

"God bless us, every one," said Tiny Tim.

"Spirit," said Scrooge, "tell me if Tiny Tim will live."

"I see a vacant seat in the poor chimney corner, and a crutch without an owner, carefully preserved. If these shadows remain unaltered by the future, the child will die."

"No, no, kind Spirit! Say he will be spared."

"Why?" returned the Ghost. "If he be like to die, he had better do it, and decrease the surplus population."

Scrooge hung his head at hearing his own words and was quite overcome with penitence and grief.

But he raised his eyes speedily on hearing his own name.

"Mr. Scrooge!" said Bob. "I wish now to propose a toast to the founder of the feast!"

"The founder of the feast, indeed!" said Mrs. Cratchit. "It should be Christmas Day on which one drinks the health of such an odious, stingy, hard, unfeeling man as Mr. Scrooge."

"My dear," was Bob's mild answer. "Christmas Day."

"I'll drink his health for your sake and the day's," said Mrs. Cratchit, "not for his. A Merry Christmas and a Happy New Year! He'll be very merry and very happy, I have no doubt!"

The family was happy, grateful, pleased with one another, and contented with the time; and when they faded in the sprinklings of the Spirit's torch, Scrooge had his eye upon them, and especially on Tiny Tim, until the last.

The Spirit did not linger here, but told Scrooge to hold his robe and, passing on, they sped away to another place.

It was a great surprise to Scrooge to hear a hearty laugh. It was a much greater surprise to recognize it as his own nephew's and to find himself in a bright, dry, gleaming room. Scrooge's niece by marriage laughed as heartily as her husband. And all their assembled friends were laughing loudly as well.

"He said that Christmas was a humbug," explained Scrooge's nephew. "He believed it, too! He's a comical old fellow, that's the truth. His wealth is no good to him. He doesn't do any good with it."

"I have no patience with him, Fred," observed Scrooge's niece.

"Oh, I have!" said Scrooge's nephew. "Who suffers by his ill whims? Himself, always. I pity him."

After a while, they played a game of Blindman's Buff. Then a game of How, When and Where. There were probably twenty people there, young and old, but they all played, and so did Scrooge, forgetting that his voice made no sound in their ears; and he sometimes came out with his guesses quite loud, and often guessed right, too.

The Ghost was quite pleased to find him in this mood, and looked upon him with such favor that Scrooge begged like a boy to be allowed to stay until the guests departed.

"Here's a new game," said Scrooge. "One half-hour, Spirit, only one!"

It was a game called Similes, where Scrooge's nephew had to begin a familiar expression, and the rest must complete it correctly within the space of five seconds. In the brisk fire of guessing, his guests had unveiled as "dry as a bone" and as "proud as a peacock" and even as "plump as a partridge," before the expression "as tight as..." provoked Fred's wife into guessing "your Uncle Scrooge's purse strings."

The proper answer, of course, was "a drum," which Scrooge had guessed long before, and Fred's wife was made to stand behind her chair as a forfeit.

"A Merry Christmas and a Happy New Year to the old man, wherever he is!" said Scrooge's nephew. "He wouldn't take it from me, but may he have it, nevertheless. Uncle Scrooge!" Then the whole scene passed away in the breath of the last word spoken by his nephew, and Scrooge and the Spirit were once more on their travels.

Much they saw, and far they went, and many homes they visited, but always with a happy end. It was a long night, if it were only a night. It was strange, too, that while Scrooge remained unaltered in his outward form, the Ghost grew clearly older.

"Are Spirits' lives so short?" asked Scrooge.

"My life upon this globe is very brief," replied the Ghost. "The time is drawing near. Look here." From the foldings of its robe, the Ghost brought forth two children. They were a boy and girl– wretched, abject, frightful, hideous, miserable. They stood shaking beneath the robe. Scrooge started back, appalled.

"Spirit! Are they yours?"

"No, they are yours. They are the children of those who walk the earth unseeing. This boy is Ignorance. This girl is Want. Beware of them both, for on their brow is written the word *doom*. They spell the downfall of you and all who deny their existence."

"Have they no refuge or resource?" cried Scrooge.

"Are there no prisons?" said the Spirit. "Are there no workhouses?" A bell tolled.

Scrooge looked about him for the Ghost, but it had disappeared. Then, as the last stroke ceased to vibrate, he beheld a solemn Phantom, draped and hooded, coming, like a mist upon the ground, toward him.

The Last of the Spirits

The Phantom was shrouded in a deep black garment, which left nothing visible, save one outstretched hand.
"I am in the presence of the Ghost of Christmas Yet to Come?" said Scrooge, fearfully.
The Spirit answered not, but pointed downward with its hand.
"Ghost of the Future! I fear you more than any specter I have seen. But lead on! Lead on! The night is waning fast, and it is precious time to me."

They scarcely seemed to enter the City, but there they were, in the heart of it. The Spirit stopped beside one little group of businessmen.

"No," said a great fat man with a monstrous chin. "I don't know much about it either way. I only know he's dead."

"When did he die?" inquired another.

"Last night, I believe."

"It's likely to be a very cheap funeral."

"I don't mind going if a lunch is provided, but I must be fed." This comment was received with a laugh.

Scrooge knew the men, and looked toward the Spirit for an explanation. He sensed that the unseen eyes were looking at him keenly. It made him shudder and feel very cold.
They left the busy scene and went into an obscure part of the town. The streets were foul and narrow, the shops and houses wretched.
In this infamous section of town, there was a low-browed, gloomy shop full of rusty keys, nails, unseemly rags, masses of corrupted fat and sepulchres of bones. Sitting among these wares was a gray-haired old man.

Scrooge and the Phantom came into the presence of this man, just as a woman with a heavy bundle entered the shop. Then another woman came in, and she was closely followed by a man in faded black.

"You couldn't have met in a better place," said old Joe, the shopkeeper. "Come into the parlor."

"Who's the worse for the loss of a few things like these?" cried one woman. "Not a dead man, I suppose."

"No, indeed," said the other woman, laughing.

"If he wanted to keep 'em after he was dead, why wasn't he natural in his lifetime? If he had been, he'd have had somebody to look after him, instead of lying gasping out his last breath there, alone by himself. Open that bundle, Joe."

Joe opened the bundle, "You'll not ask me how I came by these," said Mrs. Dilber.
"Every person has a right to care for himself. That's my motto," replied Joe.
The bundle contained odds and ends, bed curtains and linens.
"His blankets? I hope he didn't die of anything catching."
"I wasn't so fond of him that I'd loiter about if he did. Well, what's your offer?" said Mrs. Dilber.

"Spirit," said Scrooge, shuddering, "I see, I see. The case of this unhappy man might be my own. My life tends that way now. Merciful Heaven, what is this?"

He recoiled in terror, for the scene had changed, and now he almost touched a bare, uncurtained bed, on which, beneath a ragged sheet, there lay something covered up, unwatched, unwept-over, uncared-for–the body of a man.

"Spirit!" Scrooge said, "this is a fearful place. In leaving it, I shall not leave its lesson, trust me. Let us go!"

The Ghost conducted him through several dark, familiar streets. They entered poor Bob Cratchit's dwelling, and found the mother and the children seated round the fire.

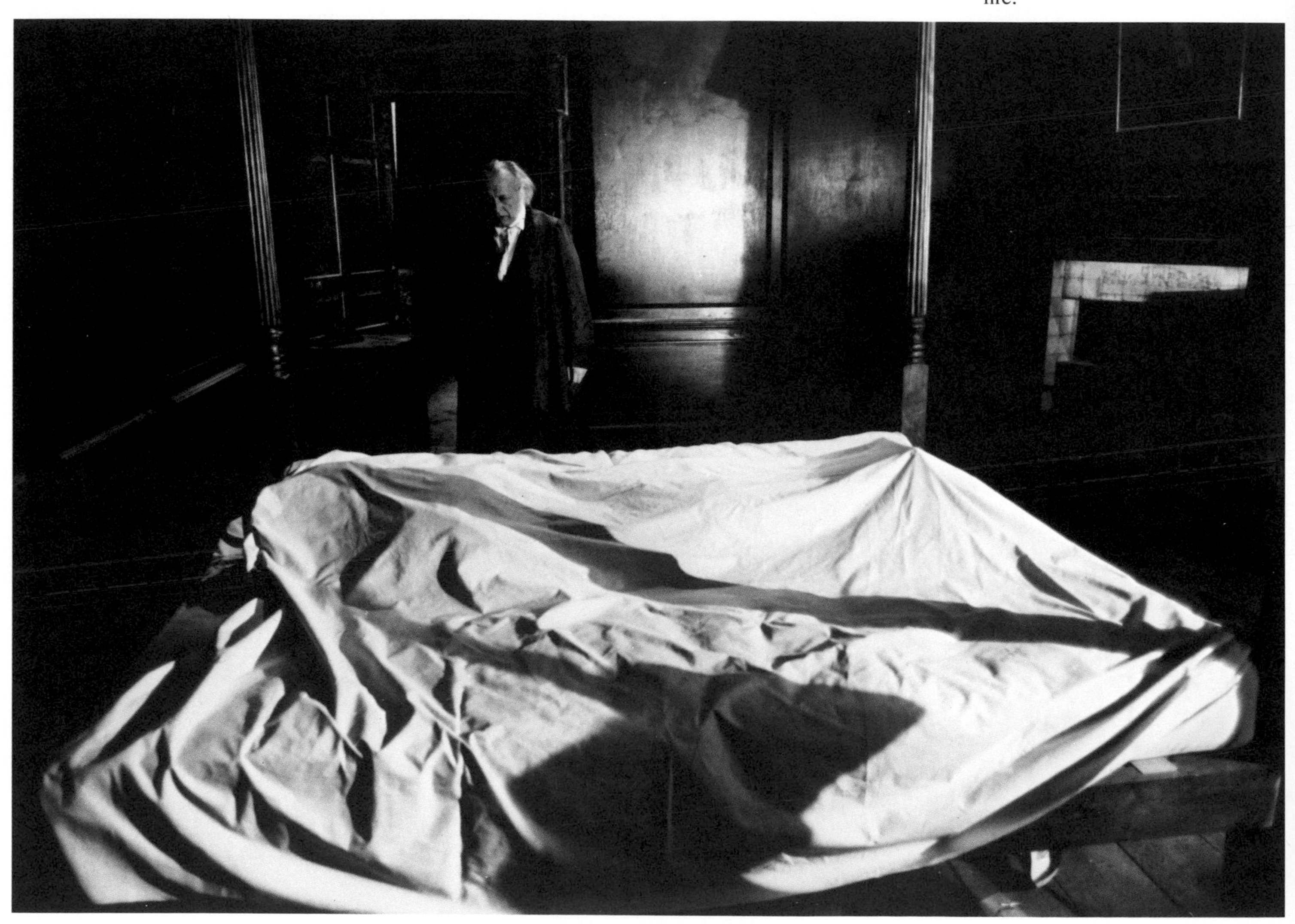

The mother laid her sewing upon the table and put her hand up to her face.

"The color hurts my eyes, and I wouldn't show weak eyes to your father when he comes home, for the world. It must be nearly time for him to arrive."

"Past it, rather," said Peter. "But I think he's walked a little slower these last few evenings, mother."

"I have known him to walk with Tiny Tim upon his shoulder," she said, "very fast indeed."

"And so have I. Often."

"But he was very light to carry, and your father loved him so, that it was no trouble. Listen! There is your father at the door!"

She hurried out to meet him, and Bob, with his shawl over his shoulders–he had need of it, poor fellow–came in. They gathered around the fire and talked. Bob told them of the extraordinary kindness of Mr. Scrooge's nephew, Fred, whom he had scarcely seen but once. "'I am very sorry for it,' he said, 'and deeply sorry for your good wife.' It really seemed he had known our Tiny Tim and felt with us."

"I'm sure he's a good soul!" said Mrs. Cratchit.

"I shouldn't be at all surprised," returned Bob, "if he got Peter a better situation."

"And then," said one of the girls, "Peter will be setting up for himself."

"It's as likely as not," said Bob. "But however and whenever we part from one another, I am sure we shall none of us forget poor Tiny Tim or this first parting that there was among us."

"Specter," Scrooge broke in, "something informs me that our parting moment is at hand. Tell me who that man was whom we saw lying dead?"

The Ghost of Christmas Yet to Come conveyed him away as before.

A churchyard.

The Spirit stood among the graves and pointed down to one.

"Before I draw nearer to that stone to which you point," said Scrooge, "answer me one question. Are these the shadows of the things that *will* be, or are they the shadows of the things that *may* be, only?" The Spirit was immovable as ever. Scrooge crept toward it, trembling as he went; and following the finger, read upon the neglected grave his own name, EBENEZER SCROOGE.

"No, Spirit! Oh, no, no! Hear me! I am not the man I was. Why show me this, if I am past all hope? Good Spirit! I will honor Christmas in my heart and try to keep it all the year. I will live in the past, the present and the future. Oh, tell me I may sponge away the writing on this stone!" In his agony, he caught the spectral hand. Holding up his hand in one last prayer, Scrooge saw an alteration in the Phantom's hood and dress. It shrunk, collapsed and dwindled down into a bedpost.

The End of It

Yes, and the bedpost was his own. The room was his own.

"My own room," gasped Scrooge. "I'm alive! I'm alive!"

"Oh, thank you, Spirits! I will keep my promise. I will live in the past, the present and the future. The Spirits of all three shall strive within me."

His hands were busy with his garments all this time, turning them inside out, putting them on upside down.

"I don't know what to do! I am as light as a feather. I am as happy as an angel. I am as merry as a schoolboy. I am as giddy as a drunken man. I don't know what day of the month it is. I don't know how long I've been among the Spirits. I don't know anything."

Running to the window, he opened it and put out his head.

"What's today?" cried Scrooge, calling down to a boy in Sunday clothes.

"Today!" replied the boy. "Why, *Christmas Day!*"

"I haven't missed it! The Spirits have done it all in one night! Of course, they can do anything they like. Hallo, my fine fellow!" he shouted to the boy. "Do you know the poulterer's in the next street but one? Do you know whether they've sold the prize turkey that was hanging up there?"

"It's hanging there now," replied the boy.

"What a delightful boy! Go and buy it. Come back with the poultryman in less than five minutes, and I'll give you half a crown!"

The boy was off like a shot.

"I'll send it to Bob Cratchit. He won't know who sent it. It's twice the size of Tiny Tim."

The chuckle with which he said this, and the chuckle with which he paid for the turkey, were to be exceeded only by the chuckle with which he sat down breathless in his chair again and chuckled until he cried.

He dressed himself in all his best and got out at last. As he walked, he saw with new eyes how the snow glistened, how happy the people were and how beautifully the carolers sang. He had a smile for all, and he received many in return.

He had not gone far when he beheld the two gentlemen who had come up to him in the Exchange on the day before to ask aid for the poor.

"My dear sirs," said Scrooge, taking the gentlemen with both hands. "A Merry Christmas to you, sirs. We met yesterday at the Exchange."

"Mr. Scrooge?"
"Allow me to beg your pardon," Scrooge continued. "And will you have the goodness..." Here Scrooge whispered in the ear of each, in turn.
"Lord bless me!" cried one of the gentleman, as if his breath were taken away. "My dear Mr. Scrooge, are you serious?"
"Not a penny less," said Scrooge.
"Please, will you come and see me?"
"We certainly will!" said the gentlemen.
In the afternoon, he made his way to his nephew's house.
"Fred!" said Scrooge.
"Why, bless my soul!" cried Fred.
"Who's that?" asked Fred's wife.
"It's your Uncle Scrooge. Will you let me in, Fred?"

Let him in! It's a wonder he didn't shake his arm off. When the welcome finally ended, Scrooge said, "I have come for three reasons. One, to beg your pardon for all I said about Christmas. That was humbug, Fred."
"It was?" Fred could not have been more astonished.
"I did not know it then, but I know it now. Second, I have come to meet your wife; and third, if that invitation to dine with you today is still in force, I accept."
"You'll be more than welcome," said Fred's wife, Janet. And they took him in to join them.
Nothing could be heartier. Wonderful party, wonderful games, wonderful unanimity, *won-der-ful* happiness!

But Scrooge was early at the office next morning. The clock struck nine. No Bob. A quarter past. No Bob. He was a full eighteen minutes behind his time.

Bob's hat was off before he opened the door; his scarf, too. He was on his stool in a jiffy, driving away with his pen as if he were trying to overtake nine o'clock.

"Mr. Cratchit," growled Scrooge. "Do you know what time it is?"

"Yes, sir," said Cratchit.

"And what time is it?"

Cratchit consulted his watch.

"Eighteen minutes past the hour, sir."

"Eighteen-and-a-half minutes past the hour. What do you mean by coming in here at this time of day?"

"I am very sorry, sir," said Bob. "I *am* behind my time. I was making rather merry yesterday, sir."

"Now, I'll tell you what, my friend," said Scrooge. "I am not going to stand for this sort of thing any longer. And therefore...I am going to...I am going to double your salary! A Merry Christmas, Bob!"
Scrooge leaped from his chair and clapped him on the back.
"I'll raise your salary and endeavor to assist your struggling family. Now make up the fires, and go buy some more coal before you dot another *i*, Bob Cratchit!"

Scrooge was better than his word. Not only did he keep it, but did infinitely more; and to Tiny Tim, who did *not* die, he was a second father. He became as good a friend, as good a master and as good a man as the good old City knew; and it was always said of him that he knew how to keep Christmas well, if any man alive possessed the knowledge. May that be truly said of us, and of all of us! And so, as Tiny Tim observed, God bless us, every one!

Frank Finlay

George C. Scott

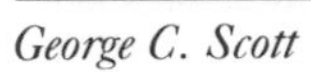

Angela Pleasence

Edward Woodward

Mark Strickson

Susannah York

Roger Rees

Anthony Walters

David Warner

Caroline Langrishe

Lucy Gutteridge

Charles W. Buss, "Dickens' Dream."
Courtesy the Trustees of the Dickens
House Museum.

Mr. Dickens and Christmas

If the residents of the comfortable houses just south of London's Regent's Park had looked down from their windows into the dark streets late at night during the months of October and early November 1843, they might have seen a man, wrapped in a greatcoat, pacing the sidewalk feverishly. As he walked, fifteen and twenty miles at a stretch, he declaimed to the night air, laughed aloud, and even wept at times. Some of the watchers might have recognized the solitary figure as their most famous neighbor, Charles Dickens. Those who knew him well would have understood that Mr. Dickens was writing again.

Dickens had always taken his imagination into the streets–and the streets into his imagination–when shaping, peopling and animating his stories. He wrote for hours at his desk each morning, often at a furious pace, to capture in ink the imaginings of his afternoon and late-night walks. And often, both before and after dinner, he would bundle himself up again and strike out into the streets. It was an exhausting method that would have killed a less energetic man, but these nocturnal ramblings and the strenuous days that followed them had produced all those extraordinary books that the English reading public devoured in installments the moment they appeared: *The Pickwick Papers*, *Oliver Twist*, *Nicholas Nickleby*, *The Old Curiosity Shop* and *Barnaby Rudge*. These works had made Dickens, while still a young man, the most famous writer in England.

The story that possessed him that winter of 1843 was not a vast three-volume novel destined to appear in serial form. It would, rather, be given to the world in a single small volume, slight in comparison to the sprawling tales that preceded it. It had no cast of thousands, no panoramic view of England, no attractive hero or winsome heroine. Its hero was also its principal villain–the chilly, sour old miser named Ebenezer Scrooge. Yet *A Christmas Carol* was to become Dickens' best-loved work, and it has remained so from his day to our own.

The first half of 1843 had been a thoroughly distressing time for Dickens. Only the year before, he had taken his first trip to America, and he had not been impressed. His book about the experience, *American Notes*, was not received with great enthusiasm by his friends in England, and in America it provoked widespread outrage. He had plunged into the writing of a sixth novel, *Martin Chuzzlewit*, but by the middle of 1843, the sales of the paperbound "Chuzzlewit" installments had begun to dip alarmingly. Desperately angling for renewed interest, he took Martin to America in a series of mercilessly funny chapters that renewed the howls for Dickens' blood from the far side of the Atlantic. The English, however, remained indifferent, and sales continued to be disappointing.

Dickens was not used to

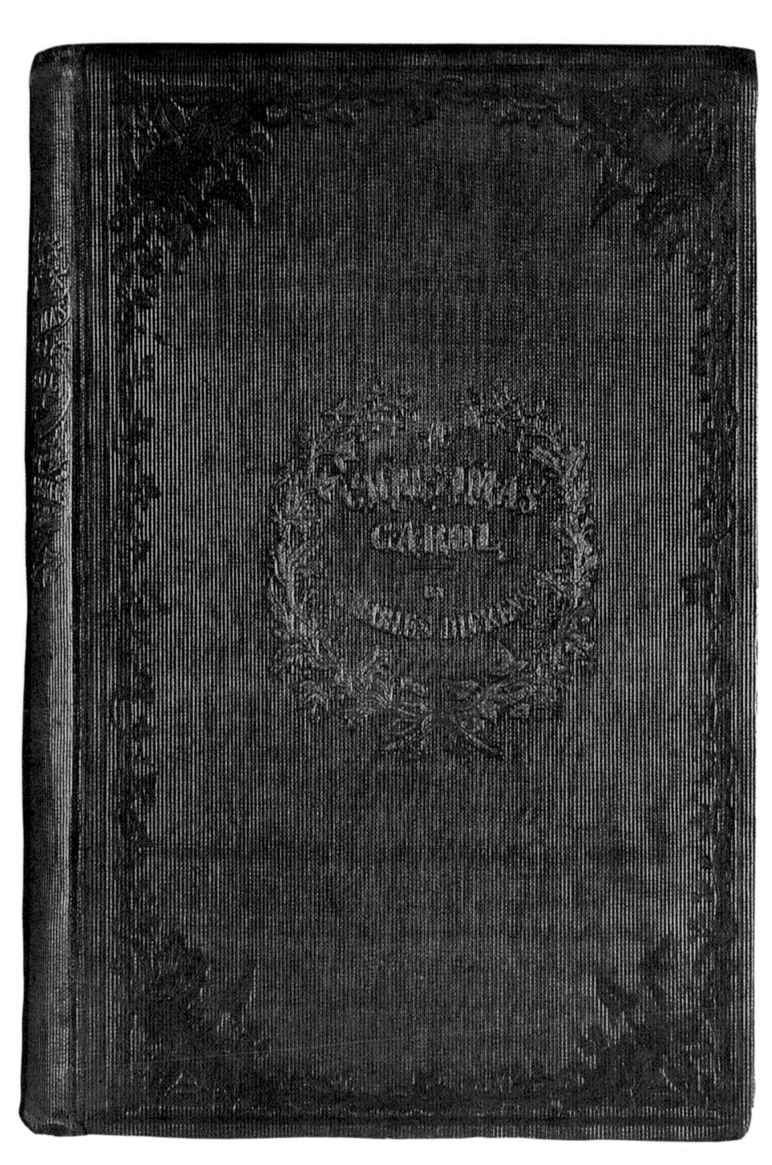

Original Cover, "A Christmas Carol" (1843). Courtesy of the Beinecke Rare Book and Manuscript Library, Yale University.

failure, and he took it to heart. Furthermore, he was, as always, under tremendous financial pressure, and a fifth child was expected. Though *Martin Chuzzlewit* was less successful than he had come to expect as England's most popular writer, Dickens nonetheless was forced to continue to write it, a process he referred to as "the Chuzzlewit agonies." By autumn, he was gloomier than he had been at any time since the days before he had become an international figure in 1837 with the publication of *The Pickwick Papers*.

Then the unexpected happened. Dickens had been considering an article about the schools in jails and about the "ragged schools" that had been set up throughout the country by untrained volunteer teachers to give England's poor children the rudiments of an education. On October 5, 1843, he went to the city of Manchester as one of the main speakers–the statesman and writer Benjamin Disraeli was another–at a fund-raising forum on the problems of the poor. In his talk, Dickens pleaded that education was the surest investment in England's future and pointed to ignorance as the greatest cause of human misery. While in Manchester, his creative processes went to work and he conceived *A Christmas Carol*, complete with the Ghost of Christmas Present and its two huddled, spectral children, Ignorance and Want.

Dickens hurried back to London and threw himself into writing the tale with an enthusiasm that all but erased the ongoing "Chuzzlewit agonies." He isolated himself from his friends and family, "exciting himself," as he later wrote, "in a most extraordinary manner" with the creation of Mr. Scrooge and his Three Spirits. He delivered the manuscript to his publishers in just six weeks.

Speed was important. Dickens saw the book as a solution to his financial problems (at least for the moment), and he was determined to get it into the shops in time for Christmas. His favorite illustrator at the time, Hablot K. Browne–"Phiz"–was busy with *Martin Chuzzlewit*, and Dickens chose John Leech to create the plates. Leech had long wanted to work with Dickens, so was delighted, and agreeable to Dickens' demand for speed, though uncertain of Dickens' somewhat extravagant plans for the volume.

As shortsighted as it may seem in retrospect, Dickens' publishers, Chapman and Hall, were lukewarm about the commercial potential of his project. They suggested publishing *A Christmas Carol* as a cheap pamphlet or perhaps in a magazine. Dickens, already unhappy with the firm, was outraged. In disdain for their timidity, he proposed a new arrangement. He would publish the tale himself, using only Chapman and Hall's production and printing facilities. He would pay all costs and keep all profits. Chapman and Hall would receive only a

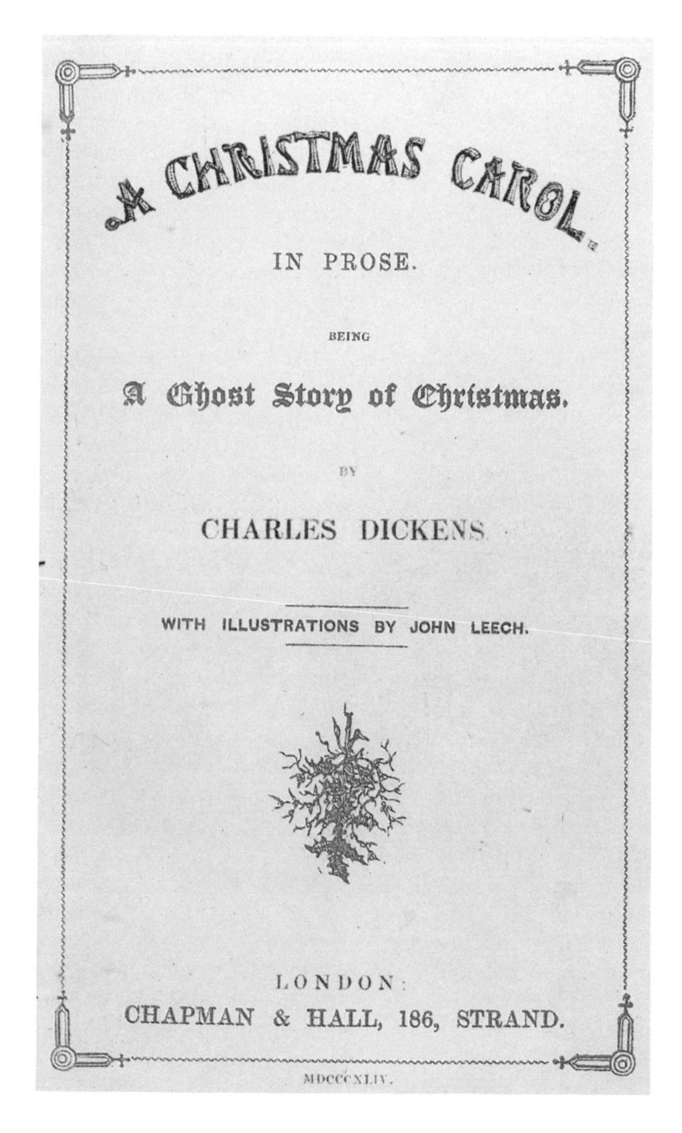

A CHRISTMAS CAROL.

IN PROSE.

BEING

A Ghost Story of Christmas.

BY

CHARLES DICKENS.

WITH ILLUSTRATIONS BY JOHN LEECH.

LONDON:

CHAPMAN & HALL, 186, STRAND.

MDCCCXLIV.

Title Page, "A Christmas Carol" (1843). Courtesy of the Beinecke Rare Book and Manuscript Library, Yale University.

small royalty, while Dickens would reap a bonanza from what he was sure would be his most popular work yet.

He leapt into the design of the book with the same enthusiasm he had devoted to its writing. Nothing but the best would do. The volume was to have gilt edges, colored endpapers, a two-color title page, a binding of red and gold, and eight illustrations–four of them in color. "In color," in Dickens' day, meant *hand*-colored, an expensive and time-consuming process. Finally, in the spirit of the season (and in the interest of higher sales), this elaborate little book was to be sold for only sixty pennies!

The first printed and bound copy arrived at Dickens' home on December 17, dangerously close to Christmas but extraordinarily fast, given the printing technology of the time. Perhaps in spite, Chapman and Hall declined to advertise it, confirming Dickens' worst view of them.

But Dickens was vindicated, immediately and triumphantly. By Christmas Day, all 6,000 copies of the first edition had been sold. By New Year's Day, a second printing had also sold out, and a third was moving briskly. A year later, at the end of 1844, more than 15,000 copies were in circulation–a figure that, considering the size of the 19th-century English book-buying public, made Dickens' brief Christmas story equivalent to the biggest of today's best sellers.

The critics were effusive. Leech's drawings, despite the artist's misgivings about the colors that were ultimately given to his plates by the hand-tinters, received almost as much acclaim as the text. Dickens' friend and literary rival, William Makepeace Thackeray, dismissed the very few critical grumbles in a lordly fashion: "Who can listen to objections to a book such as this? It seems to me to be a national benefit, and to every man and woman who reads it, a personal kindness."

Only a month earlier, Dickens had been groaning under the double burden of *Martin Chuzzlewit's* failures–artistic and commercial–but by Christmas, he was enjoying an outpouring of public affection that equaled even that of the intoxicating days of his first great triumph, *The Pickwick Papers*. He celebrated the Christmas of 1843 with extravagant abandon. He said he "broke out like a mad man. Such dinings, such dancings, such conjurings, such blindman's buffings, such theater-goings, such kissings-out of old years and kissings-in of new ones never took place before."

The new year, despite having been kissed in, brought problems. The tale's success had spawned an outbreak of literary piracy, a recurring difficulty in this time when copyright laws were virtually unenforceable. Dickens had already put up with such brazen pilfering as *The Posthumous Notes of the Pickwickian Club*, *Oliver Twiss* and *Nicholas Nickleberry*. Now no fewer than nine unauthorized dramatizations of *A Christmas Carol* played in the

Original drawing by John Leech of the Spirit of Christmas Present (1843). By permission of The Pierpont Morgan Library, New York.

London's West End theatrical district, all exploiting his genius without putting a penny into his pocket; and even music publishers were making small fortunes from collections of sheet music "inspired by" or "dedicated to" Dickens and his "Carol."

On January 6, 1844, Dickens decided to fight back. The occasion was the publication of a cheap little book called *A Christmas Ghost Story,* which claimed on its cover to have been "Re-originated from the original by Charles Dickens, Esq., and anylitically [sic] condensed for this work."

The hacks who had "condensed" the "Carol" kept every incident intact and even retained the character names, with the single exception of Fezziwig, whom, for some perverse reason, they renamed "Fuzziwig." In a particularly mystifying piece of condensation, the "re-originators" also wrote a 60-line song for Tiny Tim, inspired by Dickens' brief line, "and bye and bye they had a song, about a lost child travelling in the snow, from Tiny Tim." And in place of his masterful opening, a model of compression and mood, they offered the following:

Everybody, as the phrase goes, knew the firm of Scrooge and Marley; for, though Marley had 'long been dead' at the period we have chosen for the commencement of our story, the name of the partner still maintained its place above the warehouse door.

The combination of piracy and mutilation of his text so enraged Dickens that he declared war against the thieves and took them to court. The publishers, however, in a triumph of legal sleight of hand, declared bankruptcy and disappeared, leaving Dickens to pay more than 700 pounds sterling in court costs. This sum was almost three times as much as he had made in an entire year as a newspaper reporter.

It rankled him to pay the costs, but he was looking forward eagerly to his profits. The accounts from Chapman and Hall arrived in February. Anticipating more than 1,000 pounds sterling, he impatiently broke the seal. In place of the small fortune he had expected, he found that he had made only 230 pounds! When his court costs were figured against this sum–less than a quarter of what he had expected–*A Christmas Carol* had cost its author 470 pounds. That night, he said, he "slept as badly as Macbeth."

Ultimately, of course, he earned a good deal of money from the book. But as he packed his bags and left England for Italy that June with his family, he was disappointed and in debt. The entire experience surrounding the creation of the "Carol"–his publishers' indifference, the lack of advertising, the expenses of production, the disastrous lawsuit, the paltry profits–had drained his energies and sapped much of his inherent good nature. All in all, it is probable that no other book so good-natured in content was ever published under such a dark cloud of ill will. As he wrote to a friend, the only thing that made it bearable was the enthusiasm with which the work had been received by its readers–"the wonderful success of the book."

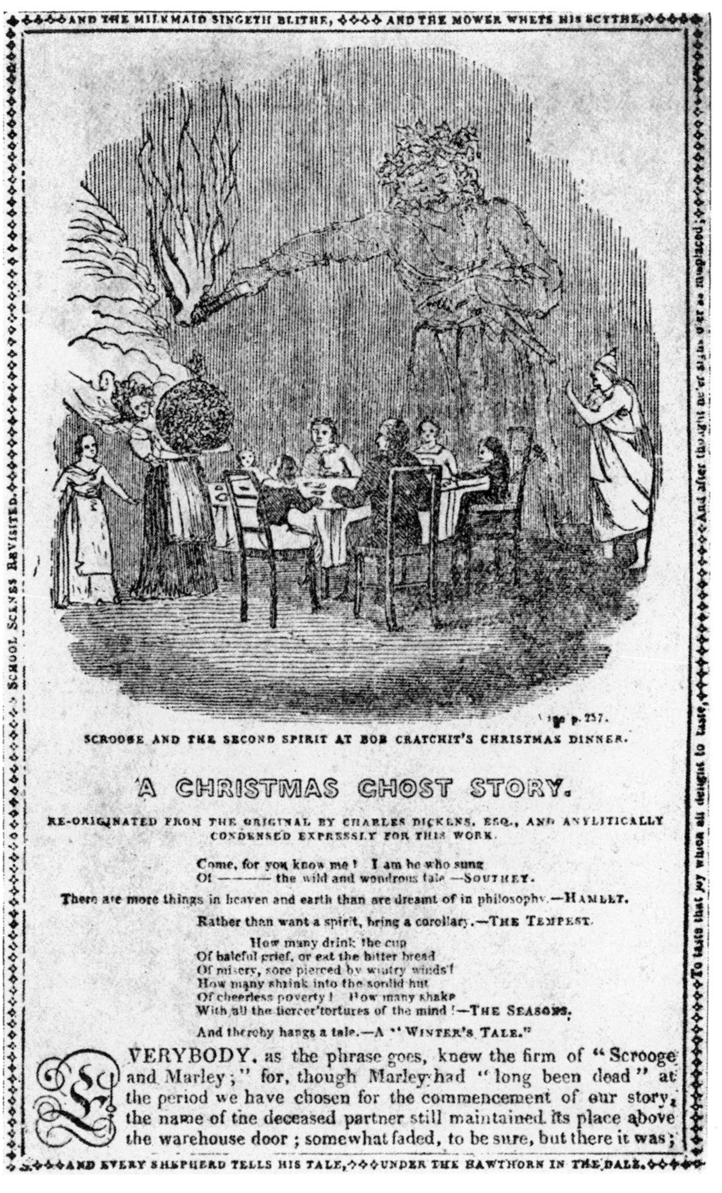

AND THE MILKMAID SINGETH BLITHE, AND THE MOWER WHETS HIS SCYTHE,

SCHOOL SCENES REVISITED.

To taste that joy which all delight to taste,

SCROOGE AND THE SECOND SPIRIT AT BOB CRATCHIT'S CHRISTMAS DINNER.

A CHRISTMAS GHOST STORY.

RE-ORIGINATED FROM THE ORIGINAL BY CHARLES DICKENS, ESQ., AND ANYLITICALLY CONDENSED EXPRESSLY FOR THIS WORK.

Come, for you know me! I am he who sung
Of ——— the wild and wondrous tale —SOUTHEY.

There are more things in heaven and earth than are dreamt of in philosophy.—HAMLET.

Rather than want a spirit, bring a corollary.—THE TEMPEST.

How many drink the cup
Of baleful grief, or eat the bitter bread
Of misery, sore pierced by wintry winds!
How many shrink into the sordid hut
Of cheerless poverty! How many shake
With all the fiercer tortures of the mind!—THE SEASONS.

And thereby hangs a tale.—A "WINTER'S TALE."

EVERYBODY, as the phrase goes, knew the firm of "Scrooge and Marley;" for, though Marley had "long been dead" at the period we have chosen for the commencement of our story, the name of the deceased partner still maintained its place above the warehouse door; somewhat faded, to be sure, but there it was;

AND EVERY SHEPHERD TELLS HIS TALE, UNDER THE HAWTHORN IN THE DALE.

The butchered plagiarism that finally provoked Dickens to file suit: the first page of "A Christmas Ghost Story." Courtesy of the New York Public Library Picture Collection.

The frontispiece of "Sketches by Boz," the first collected volume of writings by Dickens (1836).

A Christmas Carol is a high point of Dickens' long and complicated relationship with the holiday, but it would be a mistake to think of it as the only one. Dickens loved Christmas. Throughout his literary career, he turned to it again and again for subject matter and inspiration, and he always celebrated it as best he could –whether he celebrated it under circumstances happy or mournful.

In 1836, his first book, *Sketches by Boz*, was published, and one of the sketches it contained was called "A Christmas Dinner." One year later, he created the warm and uproarious Christmas celebration at Dingley Dell that is one of the many highlights of *The Pickwick Papers*. Both these pieces, while vivid, are essentially conventional observations of the Christmas holiday as an occasion for a gathering of friends and family. Despite the many memorable characters who gather at Dingley Dell, the Christmas they celebrate takes place in a closed society. Dickens makes no attempt to remind the reader that a world exists outside –a world where people are not so prosperous and comfortable, and Christmas is not so merry.

The Christmas at Dingley Dell is interrupted by the wonderful story of Gabriel Grub, a drunken church sexton who goes out into the graveyard one Christmas Eve to pursue his favorite pastime–digging a grave–and is kidnapped by the King of the Goblins. "A morose and lonely man who consorted with nobody but himself," Gabriel loathes Christmas and good cheer so deeply that his reaction to the sight of happy children celebrating the holiday is to conjure up wishful thoughts of "measles, scarlet fever, thrush, whooping-cough and a good many other sources of consolation beside."

Grub is whisked down into the goblins' enchanted cavern, where he is educated in the proper attitude toward mankind through a series of moral lessons reinforced by several hearty goblin kicks. Gabriel awakens on Christmas morning a changed man who realizes that "men like himself, who snarled at the mirth and cheerfulness of others, were the foulest weeds on the fair surface of the earth." And he comes to understand that "men who worked hard, and earned their scanty bread with lives of labor, were cheerful and happy; and that to the most ignorant, the sweet face of nature was a never-failing source of cheerfulness and joy."

Dickens borrowed the basic structure of Gabriel's story nearly six years later for *A Christmas Carol*, but he made slightly different use of it. Dickens' outlook on society had evolved during the six years that separated the two works, and he had come to see social ills as the cause of much human unhappiness. It is difficult to imagine "the sweet face of nature" bringing much cheerfulness to the two emaciated figures of Ignorance and Want who are at the center of the "Carol"; and even the reformed Gabriel, al-

"The Goblin and the Sexton," by Hablot K. Browne ("Phiz"), from "The Pickwick Papers" (1836).

though he is presumably better company than before, gives little thought to the question of human responsibility toward those whom Scrooge's nephew describes as "our fellow-passengers to the grave."

That responsibility is the subject of Scrooge's education. At the opening of *A Christmas Carol*, he denies the very notion that he might owe anything to those less fortunate than himself. Society will take care of that. Are there no prisons? And are not the workhouses in order?

His treatment of his clerk, Bob Cratchit, although comically heightened, is representative of the abuses possible in an age governed by the "iron law of wage." If Cratchit is unhappy with his position, there are thousands of equally exploitable would-be clerks eager to replace him. Dickens is vague about the precise nature of Scrooge's business; we know only that he has a "countinghouse." The miser represents a living example of dedication to profit without consideration of human cost. "Mankind was my business," says Marley's Ghost, and this is the substance of the lesson that Scrooge is taught on that enchanted Christmas Eve.

As we have seen in the picture story, the book is divided into five parts. Part one presents the unredeemed Scrooge in all his miserly glory and concludes with the warning appearance of Marley's Ghost. Part two takes Scrooge into the first stage of his education, the rediscovery of his own childhood Christmases. The Ghost of Christmas Past introduces Scrooge to the child and young man he once was and invites him to compare that compassionate, sensitive and imaginative creature with the chilly, selfish, old skinflint he has become.

Christmas Present then shows him current examples of Christmas celebrated well, and Scrooge sees these celebrations from his new and softened perspective. The last of the Spirits, the Ghost of Christmas Yet to Come uses fear–Scrooge's fear of his own mortality, the universal fear of dying alone and unloved–to complete the conversion. In the fifth part, we see the enlightened Scrooge making up for the omissions of many Christmases past.

This contrite Scrooge does not devote his life to social work; instead, he acts out his reformation on a personal level. He buys a prize turkey and sends it anonymously to the Cratchits, and he promises a large donation to the philanthropic gentlemen he had snubbed the previous day. He makes friends with the nephew he has rejected, and he gives his clerk a raise. *A Christmas Carol* was not written as social propaganda, although it certainly arose partially from social concerns. As Dickens' biographer, Edgar Johnson, says: "What Dickens has in mind is not any economic conception . . . but a feeling of the human value of human beings."

Dickens, his wife and his sister-in-law, drawn by Daniel Maclise at the time of "A Christmas Carol;" Dickens would have been about 31 years old. From the Forster Collection, the Victoria and Albert Museum.

Title page by Daniel Maclise for Dickens' third Christmas Book, "The Cricket on the Hearth" (1845).

"The Boy Scrooge," by Homer C. Appleton–a distinctly literary fantasy featuring some of Dickens' own childhood books. Courtesy of the New York Public Library Picture Collection.

If Dickens drew material from Victorian society in crafting the tale, he also drew heavily from his own life. In early childhood, he lived happily at the center of what seemed to be a solid, stable family. Then the family fortunes began to collapse. His impecunious and impractical father (later caricatured as Mr. Micawber in *David Copperfield*) fell on progressively harder times, and ended up in debtors' prison. Dickens, the most sensitive and brilliant of boys, a boy who already had dreams of greatness, was put to work in a blacking factory among men and boys with no education, no prospects, no ambition. He despaired of ever emerging from the bondage of this dismal existence. It was the grimmest period of his life, and he never completely recovered from it.

The young Scrooge, abandoned at school as Dickens himself was when his family moved from Chatham to London in 1822, reads the same books Dickens read as a boy–*Robinson Crusoe* and *The Arabian Nights*. Like Dickens, he has a sister called Fan who is allowed to remain in the bosom of the family, in sharp contrast to the young boy who feels himself an exile.

Tiny Tim, whose death was a possibility right up until the final draft of the story, echoes the childhood deaths of his brother and sister; and the Cratchits, celebrating their poor but loving Christmas, are very much like Dickens' family before they were torn apart as a result of Mr. Dickens' imprisonment. The security of the Cratchits' family circle, dependent on the whims of Mr. Scrooge, is as frail as that of Dickens' own family. Dickens had discovered, as critic Angus Wilson says, the thinness of the Victorian ice, and the story of *A Christmas Carol* mirrors that discovery:

Out from the warm bedchamber we fly into the terrible darkness, out from the warm fireside over the desolate storm-swept plains, out from the festive Christmas table to the lost children– "This Boy is Ignorance, this Girl is Want."

It is interesting to note that the work that follows *A Christmas Carol* is the most directly autobiographical of all Dickens' novels, *David Copperfield*.

For each of the next five years, with one exception, a new Christmas Book from Dickens was an annual event. In 1844, while he and his family were living in Italy, he wrote *The Chimes*. In 1845, he published *The Cricket on the Hearth* and in 1846, *The Battle of Life*. In 1847, preoccupied with the novel *Dombey and Son*, he produced nothing for the holiday; and in 1848, he concluded the series with *The Haunted Man*.

All these books were popular, although none of them quite equals the creative achievement of *A Christmas Carol*. They are all (except *The Battle of Life*) stories of reformation and rebirth, with the healing power of Christmas as the

たるなり。(194).
四一—29 Same-tap = same liquor = 同じ飲料。馬丁すらアヤヤツタほどの酒とはどんな結構な酒なりしか。(195)
四二—3 Always a delicate creature. 即ちスクルージを迎ひにきたる妹、幽靈が此女をほめて物柔らかな女であつたが氣象はエラかつたと言ふなり。(196)
四二—7 God forbid! = May God forbid from *gainsay* (イナム。モドル)。(197)
四二—12. Scrooge seemed uneasy. 流石のスクルージも斯く言はれてキマリが惡かつたものと見ゆ。(198)

のと同じ(195)注管のゾレから御辭退申したいを答へた。偖て斯固陋爺さんの革盤も此の時馬車の上よくくりつけられたので二人の子供は大喜びで校長に暇乞して、馬車に入つて庭園の周りの徑を暢々して驅り下ろした——急駛する車輪は常綠木の黑ずんだ葉から眞白な六出華を水烟のやうに散らして突進した。

『(196)一吹の風にも萎びさうな何時も物柔らかな女であつた。が、氣象は凜々としてゐた、』と幽靈が言ふ。

『さやうでござりました!』を抑へつけて言つて、『御尤な仰せ、何をして(197)背戻ませうで、決して〳〵。』

『緣づいて亡くなつたのだ。小供が有つたを思ふが。』

『一人』

『さう、お前の甥だ!』

斯固陋爺は(198)何となく氣が濟まぬやうに見ゑたが、手短かに『左や

A page from a Japanese edition of "A Christmas Carol."

redeeming force, and each involves the supernatural. Their impact in England and elsewhere was immediate, profound and lasting. Even today, Dickens and the English Christmas remain synonymous and *A Christmas Carol* is the primary reason this is so. Dickens' tale has been adapted for the stage more than twenty times and filmed nine times. The earliest film version was made in the very infancy of motion pictures at New York's Essanay Studios in 1908. The most recent production was first presented on television by IBM in 1984. Scrooge has been played by Reginald Owen, Lionel Barrymore, Alastair Sim, Albert Finney, George C. Scott–and Mr. Magoo. The story has been read publicly by Alec Guinness, Laurence Olivier, Ralph Richardson, Paul Scofield and Franklin Delano Roosevelt, and was the most popular of Dickens' own public readings. *A Christmas Carol* is a Christmas institution all over the world and there is no way to calculate how many copies, in how many languages, have been sold.

Why is it the most popular of Dickens' works? It is peopled with memorable characters, such as Scrooge himself, Cratchit and Tiny Tim, but so, of course, are all Dickens' books. It conjures up an almost tangible atmosphere –fog, cold and the supernatural– but *Great Expectations*, *Our Mutual Friend* and *Bleak House*, to name just three, create atmospheres equally convincing. It contains wonderful language, but passages as memorable are scattered throughout all of Dickens' novels, and may be found even in his letters.

The spirit of *A Christmas Carol* is probably its greatest asset. That spirit is tied closely to the meaning of the holiday–especially to the significance of giving–and this theme is almost uniquely harmonious with the spirit of the author himself. G. K. Chesterton, who loved both the *A Christmas Carol* and the man who wrote it, said:

The beauty and the real blessings of the story do not lie in the . . . repentance of Scrooge, probable or improbable; they lie in the great furnace of happiness that glows through Scrooge and everything around him; that great furnace, the heart of Charles Dickens.

The English Christmas

A sentimental view of the deposed King Charles I taking leave of his children prior to his execution, from Charles Dickens' own "A Child's History of England" (1851-53).

Although most of us cannot imagine a year without Christmas, the holiday as we celebrate it today was almost entirely shaped by the Victorian contemporaries of Charles Dickens. Without the Victorians' rediscovery of long-forgotten Christmas traditions, the English and American observation of the season would probably be very different from the joyous celebration that is now centered around the 25th of December.

In fact, in 1652, nearly two centuries before Dickens wrote *A Christmas Carol,* the celebration of Christmas was declared illegal in Britain by an Act of Parliament. With it were outlawed more than 1,000 years of British tradition of feasting, merriment and good will toward men. It was a blow from which the Christmas festivities did not fully recover until Dickens' time. In order to understand how the holiday had fallen to this disreputable state, it is necessary to go back to the seventh century.

No one is quite sure when December 25 was officially established as Christmas Day; there is no suggestion in the Bible that the birth of Jesus took place in wintertime. The early Christian church took a practical attitude toward its holidays, choosing to turn pre-existing festivals and observations to religious purpose.

By the middle of the fourth century, the Roman Catholic Church was observing both the Nativity and January 6, the Epiphany, the day on which, traditionally, the Magi arrived in Bethlehem. Between the Nativity and the Epiphany lie the famous Twelve Days of Christmas.

In Britain, the Christmas celebration was probably not popularized until 601, when Pope Gregory I–better known as Gregory the Great–instructed Augustine, his missionary to the Anglo-Saxons, to claim the local midwinter festival, called "Yule" in some parts of Britain, as a Christian holiday. Many of the indispensable trappings of Christmas as we now know it–for example, holly, mistletoe and the Yule log–were simply incorporated into the new celebration.

The Twelve Days of Christmas were firmly established in Britain by the ninth century, the time of Alfred the Great. King Alfred actually made it illegal for anyone to work during the Twelve Days and observed his own law so rigidly that, according to tradition, he lost an important town to the Danes because he refused to go into battle during the holy days.

But as British Christmas traditions became established, the stricter members of the clergy grew increasingly uneasy. They were aware of the pagan origins of many Christmas practices. Mistletoe, for example, had for so long played a part in fertility rites that it was banned from time to time in British churches. And the purely secular traditions of feasting, drinking and good fellowship seemed inappropriate during a time of solemn religious observance.

Nowhere was Christmas celebrated more vigorously than at the royal court, and never did any English monarch throw himself more wholeheartedly into the festive spirit than did Henry VIII. After establishing himself as Supreme Head of the Church of England in 1533, Henry made the holiday season the unchallenged social highlight of the court calendar and, under him and his daughter, Elizabeth I, Christmas became a marathon of feasting, dancing and attending plays.

When the Stuarts, in the person of James I, assumed the throne after the death of Elizabeth in 1603, the revels continued. Along with the plays and the dancing–scandalous enough to some–there was gambling on a truly royal scale. Henry VIII had drawn special funds directly from the treasury to cover his gambling losses; under James I, no one with less than 300 pounds sterling was admitted to the Christmas gaming table. Drinking and feasting occupied entire days.

Half a century after the death of Queen Elizabeth, on Christmas Eve of 1652, Oliver Cromwell, the nation's new Puritan Lord Protector, gave his subjects a dour Christmas present: He outlawed all observation of the holiday. He and his armies had deposed the imprudent Stuart king Charles I, and the celebration of Christmas and the first reign of the Stuarts ended only a few years apart. Puritan opposition to Christmas was not confined to Britain. The Puritans who settled Massachusetts actually enacted a law making it compulsory to work on Christmas Day.

Of course, Cromwell's opposition to Christmas arose not from any objections to its Christian significance, but from its ancient pagan origins and the excesses that had more recently marked its celebration. The prohibition prevailed for almost ten years, until 1661, after the Restoration of the monarchy, with the coronation of Charles II. In the words of a versifier of the day:

Now thanks to God for Charles' return,
Whose absence made old Christmas mourn;
For then we scarcely did it know,
Whether it Christmas were or no.

But the damage had been done. Christmas under Charles II and his successors was a pale imitation of its boisterous pre-Cromwell ancestor. Furthermore, many clergymen still opposed its celebration. As late as 1819, one unlucky Scottish lady, surprised in the middle of cooking Christmas dinner by an unannounced visit from her minister, hid the incriminating meal under the bed. Unfortunately, the iron pot, which was glowing red from sitting directly on the coals, set her bed on fire.

Christmas continued to wane during the early days of the Industrial Revolution. In fact, in that work-oriented world, holidays disappeared from the calendar at an alarming rate. In 1761, the Bank of England closed for 47 holidays each year. In 1825, it observed 40 holidays; and in 1834, three years before Victoria's coronation, it closed for only four.

Many workers were given only a half-day off on December 25, and some received no time off at all. The law was a bit more lenient for the many children who toiled twelve-hour days: It specified that they were to receive two full holidays each year, Christmas and Good Friday. By the beginning of the 19th century, Christmas had all but disappeared as an important celebration in London.

But the Victorians prized sentiment and held the family sacrosanct, and the celebration of Christmas was a harmonious expression of both these values, as well as an opportunity to focus loving attention upon children. In an apparent contradiction, the same society that allowed children to work long, grueling days under appalling and often dangerous conditions also sentimentalized and idealized the young. Under Victoria, the old Christmas traditions were rediscovered, and children were made the center of the celebration. By the end of the 19th century, Dickens' contemporaries had transformed the pallid holiday they inherited into the Christmas we celebrate today.

Not that the modern Christmas is a wholly British invention: The British felt free to accept contributions from abroad. From Germany, for example, came the Christmas tree, introduced into England early in the 19th century by the Hanoverian royal family. Year after year, the British public followed and faithfully imitated the progress of Christmas as celebrated by Queen Victoria and her German-speaking Saxon consort, Prince Albert, who was personally responsible for the British popularity of the tree.

Santa Claus arrived in England by a more indirect route. America's Dutch settlers brought with them to the New World the figure of St. Nicholas, based on a semi-legendary, fourth-century bishop who saved destitute girls from unhappy fates by providing them with dowries that allowed them to marry respectably. In one famous version of the tale, he dropped his gift of gold down the chimney, giving rise to a far-reaching Christmas tradition.

By the 16th century, St. Nicholas was firmly established in Holland as the bearer of gifts on Christmas Eve. When the Dutch came to New York, they named their first church after him. Their non-Dutch neighbors transformed the saint that the Dutch called Sint Niklaas or, colloquially, Sinter Klaes into the Americanized Santa Claus. In 1822, a New York college professor named Dr. Clement C. Moore wrote a poem for his children entitled "A Visit From St. Nicholas," a copy of which was sent (without Dr. Moore's permission or knowledge) to the newspapers. Illustrator Thomas Nast, otherwise best known as one of the fathers of the political cartoon, visualized Dr. Moore's jolly, chimney-descending old elf, and the modern Santa Claus was born. The rotund

Thomas Nast, one of the inventors of the political cartoon, also gave shape to our modern image of Santa Claus in drawings such as this one. Courtesy of the New York Public Library Picture Collection.

Poor London carolers in an 1836 engraving by Robert Seymour. Courtesy of the New York Public Library Picture Collection.

American Santa gradually became more popular in England than the rowdier (and thinner) Father Christmas.

The Victorians unified all these elements, added their own rediscovered traditions, and simultaneously turned the celebration inward, toward the family, and outward to others, in the spirit of charity for one's fellow human beings. The holiday had a special significance for the many social reformers, like Dickens, who championed the cause of the poor. For them, "good will toward men" meant especially good will toward the less fortunate, the destitute, the debtors, the teeming multitude of Victorian castoffs. The two philanthropic gentlemen who call unsuccessfully on Scrooge at the beginning of Dickens' story are operating very much in the new Victorian tradition of making Christmas, as Scrooge's nephew says,

a kind, forgiving, charitable, pleasant time; the only time I know of, in the long calendar of the year, when men and women seem by one consent to open their shut-up hearts freely, and to think of people below them as if they really were fellow-passengers to the grave, and not another race of creatures bound on other journeys.

To provide musical accompaniment for this national outpouring of emotion, the Victorians rediscovered those traditional songs of joy, Christmas carols. Caroling had been in danger of extinction at the beginning of the 19th century; only "God Rest Ye Merry, Gentlemen" was well-known in the cities, and many of the old carols survived only in "odd nooks," as the poet Tennyson said, where Christmas was well-remembered. But the Victorians made Christmas musical once again, a harmonious celebration of a harmonious time of the year. Charles Dickens paid an eternal tribute to the power of this holiday music with the title of the first and greatest of his Christmas Books.

"Awaiting Admission to the Casual Ward," Sir Luke Fildes (1843-1927). Courtesy Royal Halloway College, University of London.

Gathering the evergreens; an American view by Winslow Homer. Courtesy of the New York Public Library Picture Collection.

Christmas by Hand: Victorian Holiday Crafts and Traditions

Christmas in Charles Dickens' time was, first and foremost, a family celebration. The Victorians made one of their greatest contributions to the modern shape of the holiday when they focused the Christmas celebration on their children. In Dickens' own evergrowing household (Mrs. Dickens gave birth to ten children), the holiday season was a frantic whirl of parties, games and gifts; and even though Victorian children were taught to "know their place," they also knew that their place, at Christmastime, was very much in the center of things.

More than any other time of the year, Christmas allowed children to take part in all the activities of the family. For those few shining weeks, the usual regimentation of household tasks–divided between adults and children, and, in more affluent homes, between employers and servants–dissolved into a glorious anarchy of collective effort. There was *so much* to be done! The house had to be decorated; Christmas cards had to be made and sent; the tree had to be selected, put up and trimmed; gifts had to be created or chosen, and given; and all this (or at least most of it) had to be done by hand.

We tend to think of the Victorian Christmas with nostalgia, and most of us feel that the holiday we celebrate today is a much more commercial affair than it was in Dickens' time. Nevertheless, Christmas advertising had become an important economic fact of life within fifteen years of the writing of *A Christmas Carol*. Critics of the practice even then expressed fears that the holiday was in danger of losing its meaning. By the 1860s, toys were sold by the tens of thousands all over Britain; shops issued special Christmas catalogues; and newspapers and magazines became thick and unwieldy as the approach of Christmas inspired page after page of enticing advertisements.

At home, practically everything still had to be done by hand. And most of the pleasant tasks imposed by the season were shared among adults and children alike as a living demonstration of the power of the season to unite people in love and joy.

Families all over the world have discovered that planning and celebrating a "Victorian Christmas"–complete with a reading of *A Christmas Carol*–can, even today, bring people closer together. It can also lead to a rediscovery of the traditions behind the holiday that we often now take for granted.

Deck the Halls: Decorating the House

Christmas Greenery

At the upper end of the room, seated in a shady bower of holly and evergreens, were the two best fiddlers, and the only harp, in all Muggleton. In all sorts of recesses, and on all kinds of brackets, stood massive old silver candlesticks with four branches each. The carpet was up, the candles burnt bright, the fire blazed and crackled on the hearth . . . .

As this passage from *The Pickwick Papers* suggests, greenery and light were the essential elements of Victorian Christmas decoration. Both were beautiful in and of themselves, and both were rich in symbolic meaning.

In ancient times, all over Europe, evergreens were associated with nature's continual rebirth and, by extension, with the concepts of spiritual renewal and immortality. As Christianity's influence spread, it was natural for these beautiful, fragrant plants to become linked with the new religion's promise of immortality.

Initially, the early Christian church in England, mindful of the pagan associations of evergreens, resisted the practice of bringing greenery into places of worship at Christmastime. But the ancient tradition was too compelling, and churchmen who had been nurtured among the people were inclined to overlook or conveniently forget the prohibition. Eventually, most British churches were decorated with evergreens during the holiday season. One chronicler in the 1500s wrote that at the "time of Christmas, every man's house, as also their parish churches, were decked with ivy, bay, and whatsoever the season afforded to be green."

For the Victorians, no house was ready for Christmas entertaining unless it was strewn with greenery, redolent with the sharp scent of fir, pine and cedar, gleaming with holly and ivy. Each plant had its own tradition, and each was used in special ways.

Holly, during the reign of the Roman Emperors, was thought to be a particularly appropriate gift during the Roman Saturnalia, brought to England by occupying Roman troops and celebrated during the time of year later designated as Christmas. Later, European folk traditions identified the holly plant as the source of a syrup that could supposedly cure winter coughs and induce good dreams when hung at the head of the bed. For the Victorians, holly was used lavishly, usually in clusters that emphasized the contrast between the bright red berries and the dark green luster of the leaves–the traditional colors of Christmas.

Here are some easy 19th-century decorating ideas using holly. By the way, it's always a good idea, when working with this very prickly plant, to wear gloves.

Candle clusters: You will need a wire coat hanger, thin green wire, wire cutters and pliers, in addition to a quantity of fine dark holly. Straighten the hanger and cut a length long enough to make a circle about eight inches in diameter. Curve the wire into a circle, bend the ends back and interlock them.

Now bind the holly, one sprig at a time, to the hanger, using the fine green wire. (Actually, dark plastic bag-ties can be used just as easily.) Arrange the next branch over the preceding one so that the wire is hidden, and proceed in this fashion until you have constructed a thick circle of holly. It should be two-to-three inches thick, and all the holly should point in the same direction.

Your holly cluster should be big enough to put a thick white candle (on a low holder) into the center, leaving no less than a full inch between the candle and the holly in all directions.

Two or three such candle clusters will brighten any holiday table.

Holly wreaths: The Christmas wreath made partially of holly is perhaps the most beautiful ornament that can be hung on a door to celebrate the festive season. There are many ways to make wreaths, but here is one of the simplest. You will need two large pieces of heavy cardboard, a staple-gun, fine dark-colored wire, dark green paint or paper (green plastic will do, but it must be hidden), and a healthy assortment of greens and other decorations: holly, pine branches, pine cones, walnuts, cranberries–any winter growth you think will look appropriate.

First, let the foliage set by placing the stems in warm water for twelve hours or more. This will keep the greens fresh for a longer period.

While the greens are setting, draw a circle, approximately eighteen inches in diameter, on each of the pieces of cardboard. The center hole should be about six inches in diameter. Cut around the large circles on each piece of cardboard, then cut out the center hole. Glue the two pieces of cardboard together, overlaying them so that the corrugations run at right angles. Let the glue dry thoroughly.

Now paint the cardboard green with a dark tempera paint–

don't forget the edges–or wrap it with dark green paper or plastic. Using the staple-gun, fasten evergreen clippings to the cardboard until you have built up a thick base. The branches should overlap so that the staples are invisible. When the cardboard is hidden and the wreath has a satisfactory thickness, wrap thin wire around sprigs of holly and twist the wire-ends around the sturdier evergreen stems, placing the holly evenly around the wreath.

Wire can be passed through firm cranberries and the cranberries wired into place, and pine cones can be scattered throughout and fastened with wire. If you wish, you can even fasten Christmas tree ornaments to the wreath. To hang, make a heavy loop of wire at the top of the wreath, and cover it with a bow of bright gift ribbon.

Holly trimmings: Holly can also be used as a trim for the edges of mirrors or pictures, fastened in place with transparent tape; or it can be stitched loosely onto the edges of curtains as a colorful holiday border. Many Victorian households trimmed all drapes and curtains with a combination of holly and dried ferns that had been pressed flat in books months earlier for that very purpose.

Ivy was strongly associated with the god of wine, Bacchus, and played a part in all his festivals during the long Roman occupation of Britain. This was a particularly unfortunate association in the eyes of the early church, but it fit in perfectly with the feasting and drinking that marked the early Christmas holidays.

The Victorians used ivy profusely, usually as a trim for mirrors, pictures and window ledges. They chose the youngest and shiniest trailers, and washed them in warm, slightly soapy water to rid them of anything that might be on the undersides of the leaves–spider-egg cases, for example. Once the greenery was clean and shining, they twisted it around banisters or down the chains that supported chandeliers, and they tacked it to the edges of mantels and doorways. Long tendrils of ivy were sometimes woven into crowns and victory wreaths for the winners of the parlor games described in the next chapter.

Pine, cedar and *fir* were prized in the past for their pungent wintry fragrance, still associated with Christmas today because of the Christmas tree. Their dark feathery foliage softened the familiar contours of drawing rooms and dining rooms, giving them a fairyland quality, especially by candlelight.

In Europe, the branches of these evergreen trees had been gathered and brought indoors as a tradition for thousands of years. In addition to their symbolism and beauty, they had a purely practical value: Their perfume refreshed the stale air of rooms that had been shut up for long damp months. Often the herb rosemary, preserved since summer, was scattered with the evergreens to add a new scent to the wintertime bouquet. But most Victorians were not fond of rosemary, and this custom waned in Dickens' day. Nevertheless, you may want to incorporate rosemary (now available, fresh, year-round) into your Christmas planning.

As important as holly and ivy were, they were used mainly as decorative accents by Dickens and his contemporaries. Evergreen branches were the main ingredient, and they were used everywhere.

Garlands are festive, beautiful, easy to make and versatile. To create your own, you'll need dark green cord (nylon clothesline will work perfectly well), fine wire, wire cutters and gloves–and lots and lots of evergreen sprigs, preferably of different kinds. You can put laurel and bay into garlands as well. It's a good idea to let the evergreens sit in water for twelve hours or more before weaving them onto the garlands.

Using the cord on which you plan to wind the garlands, measure the areas where you intend to hang them–in doorways, around windows, radiating out from central hanging light fixtures to the junctures of walls and ceilings. Remember that you will want your garlands to form a graceful curve, so allow extra rope for each measurement.

Using three or four lengths of greenery each time, tie them

tightly to the cord with the wire, twisting the wire several times and cutting off the ends closely to eliminate needle-sharp points. (You can, if you wish, dispense with the wire altogether by using green gardening cord, but knotting it is more time-consuming than twisting the wire.)

Place a second bunch of foliage beneath the ends of the first so that the wire (or cord) is hidden. Make the garland full and heavy, and make sure that all the evergreens are pointing in the same direction. When all the greens are in place, you can wire cranberries or other bright berries to the garland by passing the wire through the center of the berry and twisting it around a sturdy evergreen twig.

The garlands will be heavy, so anchor them well to strong fixtures. You can wrap them around banisters or trim the outside of your front door.

A *garland curtain* is an especially festive touch for any open archway or double door. Simply hang garlands from the top of the door to the bottom, creating a fragrant, feathery curtain of evergreens through which a lighted Christmas tree looks magical and tantalizing to a child on the other side. For curtains, or for any garlands that are likely to be touched often, you may want to use green gardening cord rather than wire.

Table decorations: You can make even the simplest table look more festive by strewing loose evergreen branches down its center, especially on a white tablecloth. Pine cones, apples and oranges will add to the overall effect, as well as to the fragrance the decoration produces. Combine this decorating scheme with one or two of the holly candle clusters described earlier to produce a table Dickens himself would have recognized with delight.

Evergreen bouquets can be arranged in large vases for display anywhere in the house where flowers would be placed in warmer months. The Victorians used long sprays of particularly fragrant evergreens such as cedar, often with cones still attached, and added to them brilliant autumn leaves which had been picked at the height of their color and pressed in books or stacks of newspaper. Pressed ferns can also be used for a more delicate effect.

Mistletoe was the most sacred plant of all in pagan times, the "golden bough" central to so much European mythology. It lives parasitically on oak trees and flourishes without ever touching the ground; to some people it seemed to represent a link between earth and heaven.

For the Romans and the early Scandinavians, it was the plant of peace and healing; enemies who encountered each other beneath it were obliged to lay down their weapons and swear a truce. The curative powers of mistletoe were so highly esteemed that it was called "allheal" in some coun-

The mistletoe works its spell: "Christmas Eve at Mr. Wardle's," by Hablot K. Browne ("Phiz"), from "The Pickwick Papers" (1836).

tries. It was regarded as a powerful charm against evil.

Mistletoe however, was best known as a symbol of fertility. This association was so strong that it was rarely permitted inside churches in Britain. Nevertheless, there was hardly a home that didn't have mistletoe during the holiday season . . . for good reason:

It hath been writ that any man
May blameless kiss what lass he can,
Nor anyone shall say him "no"
Beneath the holy mistletoe.

The delightful tradition of the Christmas kiss beneath the mistletoe seems to have been a purely British invention. Dickens himself enjoyed it as well as or better than most, and his delight in the custom is evident in the famous Chistmas sequence at Dingley Dell that enlivens *The Pickwick Papers:*

From the center of the ceiling of this kitchen, old Wardle had just suspended with his own hands a huge branch of mistletoe, and this same branch of mistletoe instantaneously gave rise to a scene of general and most delightful struggling and confusion; in the midst of which Mr. Pickwick . . . took the old lady by the hand, led her beneath the mystic branch, and saluted her in all courtesy and decorum.

Although the unadorned mistletoe bough was probably the most frequent manifestation of the tradition, more elaborate and ornamental variations were also in evidence.

The *kissing ring* was one of these. To make it, all you will need is heavy wire, thinner wire for tying on the boughs, gloves, wire cutters, evergreens and a large bunch of mistletoe, as well as anything you would like to attach for extra charm: oranges, walnuts or apples, for example.

Shape the wire into a large circle or two, bend back the ends and interlock them. Using the thinner wire, twine the evergreens around the loops until they are substantially filled out. Hang fruit or nuts inside the circle or fasten them onto its rim. If you have made two circles, place one inside the other at right angles to suggest a sphere. The ring can be decorated further with ribbons or colored cutouts from Christmas cards. Finally, suspend the mistletoe cluster from the bottom of the hoop.

When you are satisfied, hang the ring from the highest rafter or light fixture and wait for the fun to begin.

Traditionally, all Christmas greenery was taken down by Twelfth Night (January 6). In fact, it was thought to be bad luck to leave it hanging longer than that. Often the decorations, which were dry and highly inflammable by then, were burned in the fireplace in a fragrant conflagration.

The poet Robert Herrick, in the 17th century, commemorated the removal of the greenery in these lines:

Down with the Rosemary, and so
Down with the Bays and Mistletoe.
Down with the Holly, Ivy, all,
Wherewith we dressed the Christmas hall.

Light

Light was the second great component of Victorian Christmas decoration. Light had long represented life itself, and it evolved during the Christian era into a symbol of Christ himself.

For centuries, the great Christmas source of light and heat–especially in the manor homes with their great fireplaces–was the Yule log. A massive chunk of wood, usually oak but sometimes birch or ash, the Yule log was lighted on Christmas Eve and–if good fortune prevailed–continued to burn until Twelfth Night.

In some places, the log was soaked with wine and spices or decorated with greenery. In parts of France, the Yule log was even thought to be the source of the children's presents. It was carried into the house covered in a rough cloth and, before it was kindled, the children would beat it with sticks, crying: "Come forth! Come forth!" When gifts failed to appear, the children were sent outside briefly to confess their sins of the preceding year. When they returned, their presents were scattered in front of the fireplace. A piece of last year's Yule log was then used to set the log afire. That year-old piece of wood was often kept in the house as an apparent safeguard against lightning, probably a nod toward the tradition's origins: In the Scandinavian countries, possessing a burnt log was regarded as a way to ensure the good will of the god Thor, whose thunderbolt would not strike burnt wood.

With the massive movement of people from the countryside to the city during the Industrial Revolution, the tradition of Yule log became but a faint memory. City fireplaces could not accommodate the massive log, yet the fire remained the focus of family activities, even for urban families in Dickens' time. The Cratchits gather to drink their seasonal toasts from their chipped glassware in front of the fire, and the fireplace "sends forth a rich glow" as songs are sung and goblin stories told at Dingley Dell.

The Victorians loved a crackling fire, and although coal was the most plentiful fuel in offices and factories, for a Christmas gathering the home grate was likely to be piled high with a mixture of pine and hardwood–the pine for heat and kindling, the hardwood for duration.

As we have seen in the excerpt from *The Pickwick Papers*, candles played an important role in the festival of light that was the Victorian Christmas. In addition to their purely practical function as interior lighting in homes not equipped with gas, candles had an obvious religious significance.

The candle's flame was not only a symbol of light, but of truth and enlightenment. In Victorian times, it also came to symbolize concern for the poor. A candle placed in the window throughout the Twelve Days of Christmas told any lost or homeless traveler that food and shelter would be found within. It would have been unthinkable to have turned anyone away during the Twelve Days of Christmas.

But of course, the candles that most strike the imagination when we conjure up a Victorian Christmas are the slender tapers that illuminate the Christmas tree.

J.A. Fitzgerald, "The Private View" (1865). Courtesy of the New York Public Library Picture Collection.

The Tree

The idea of the Christmas tree came to England from Germany. Queen Victoria's royal consort, Prince Albert, is often given credit for introducing it; but it was Victoria and Albert's tree, first set up in Windsor Castle in 1841 (two years before Dickens wrote *A Christmas Carol*), that made the custom immediately fashionable among the British. Albert himself contributed further to the spread of the tradition by giving decorated trees to army barracks and schools.

Prince Albert's royal Christmas tree was seven feet tall and was placed, in European style, on a table that made it even taller. The glistening angel at its tip towered almost eleven feet from the floor, high above the crowned heads that gathered around it on Christmas Eve.

The Christmas tree tradition is an ancient one; in fact, trees with gifts tied to them played a part in the Roman Saturnalia celebration. The custom seems first to have been adapted to the Christmas celebrations in Germany. Records from the 14th and 15th century tell us that a pine tree with apples tied to it was a customary prop in the miracle plays enacted in front of cathedrals during the Christmas season. This "Paradise Tree" represented the Tree of Life in the Garden of Eden, and from it, in the plays, Eve plucked the Fruit of Knowledge and gave it to Adam. In northern Germany, until almost 100 years ago, many people continued to place little figures of Adam, Eve and the serpent beneath the family tree.

By the time Prince Albert popularized the Christmas tree in England, it had become a child's delight: Candy dangled from every bough, candles gleamed and presents nestled in its branches. Like most Englishmen, Dickens was captivated with the new custom, and he embraced it as enthusiastically as he did roast goose and "God Rest Ye Merry, Gentlemen." In 1859, he wrote:

I have been looking on, this evening, at a merry company of children assembled round that pretty German toy, a Christmas tree. The tree was brilliantly lighted by a multitude of little tapers; and everywhere sparkled and glittered with bright objects. There were rosy-cheeked dolls, hiding behind green leaves; and there were jolly, broad-faced little men, much more agreeable in appearance than many real men–and no wonder, for their heads came off and showed them to be full of sugarplums; there were fiddles and drums; there were witches standing in enchanted rings of pasteboard, to tell fortunes; there were humming tops, needle cases, pen wipers, bouquet holders, imitation apples, pears, walnuts crammed with surprises.

The tree was a source for many of the children's presents, as well as being a kind of temporary fairyland that embodied the spirit of the holiday.

For a few days, the tree became the center of family life. On it hung ornaments that had been made mostly by hand by family members. They were reused from season to season as tangible recollections of the Spirit of Christmas Past.

Here are a few authentic Victorian ornaments your family may wish to create for your own Christmas tree.

Good Fortune Chain: This is a decoration the whole family can make. You will need multicolored gift-wrap paper that is white on one side, glue, gold paper and pens. Each member of the family cuts strips of gift-wrap paper about four inches long and one inch wide. On some of these strips they write fortunes or good wishes for the coming year. Then all the strips of paper are twisted into loops and glued so they interlock.

Make gold paper loops to place on either side of the "fortune links." Attach enough links to make a good-sized garland and drape the tree with it. No one will know what the fortunes are until the tree is taken down; then each member of the family can choose a fortune link, break it, and read his or her own personal Christmas fortune.

Other garlands can be created by stringing the old standbys, popcorn and cranberries, or by wrapping peanuts in colored paper–use several colors–and tying gold cord around the pinched middle of each. Simply cut the paper into three-to-four-inch squares and roll a paper square around each peanut. Twist the ends, and then loop and tie the cord around the center, leaving two or three inches of cord between each pair of peanuts.

A *pomander*–a piece of dried fruit studded with cloves–can add fragrance to even the freshest tree. You must make your pomander at least two weeks before you intend to use it, but once it is made, it will last for years.

You will need an apple or an orange, a box of cloves, some powdered cinnamon, a thimble, a paper bag and–ultimately–some ribbon. Using the thimble on your thumb, push the cloves into the apple or orange until it is completely covered. Then put it into the paper bag with a couple of tablespoons of ground cinnamon and shake it for a moment.

Put the bag in a dark, warm place–a kitchen drawer will do–for about two weeks. At the end of that time, the fruit should be hard and fragrant. Shake the loose cinnamon from it and wrap with ribbon, leaving the ends loose at the top. Tie the ends in a bow over a strong bough of the tree.

Eggs can be used to make light and delicate ornaments, but they must be blown first to remove the contents. To do this, take fresh eggs at room temperature and carefully punch a hole at each end with a pin. Enlarge the holes slightly by wiggling the pin in the hole. Now put your lips to the narrow end of the egg and blow with all your might.

When the last of the white and yolk have come out of the shell, wash and dry the egg gently. Christmas scenes or motifs can then be painted on the shell with watercolors, or it can be dipped into dye or even sprayed gold. You can create an interesting (if not authentically Victorian) variegated effect by melting several crayons in hot water and carefully dipping the eggshell into the pan so the floating wax adheres to the surface. To do this, pass a thin skewer through the two holes in the eggshell, dip it into the water, and turn it back and forth. Leave the shell on the skewer and stand it up in a jar or glass until it dries. For the best effect, you should use at least one metallic crayon. You should consider heating the water and crayons in an old pan rather than a new one; the melted crayons can be cleaned up with scouring powder and hot water, but it is something of a chore.

Other tree-decorating ideas include cookies and gingerbread men, cut-out figures from Christmas cards, paper stars, hard candies, bright ribbon bows, apples, oranges, nuts (both natural and painted), colored envelopes containing Christmas letters to members of the family–almost anything that is bright, attractive and light in weight.

The tree should contain at least one gift for every member of the family. Half the fun for Victorian children was peering through the laden and colorful branches of the tree to spy a tiny package with their name on it or an unwrapped toy in answer to their Christmas dreams.

The Royal Christmas Tree; this etching of Victoria and Albert's Christmas tree was first published in 1848 and helped greatly to popularize the tree in England. A slightly altered and "Americanized" version was published the following year in the United States.

Victorian Gift-Giving

The Victorian attitude concerning gifts was that the thought was more important than the present. Each Christmas gift was both an expression of love and a celebration of the act of giving, and the Victorians excelled in exchanging gifts in a creative and often amusing manner. Here are three authentic suggestions from Dickens' time.

A *cobweb party* can turn gift-giving into a frenzied, laughter-filled search as all members of the family pick their way through a room crisscrossed with colored yarn in an effort to trace the yarn in their particular color to the present waiting at the other end. You will need the gifts, a large ball of different colored yarn for each family member, and lots of time and patience.

Simply assign one color to each person and tie yarn of that color to each of his or her presents. Make a multicolored web of yarn all over the room, passing the yarn under and over furniture, wrapping it around chair and table legs, and under cushions. Presents can be hidden or in plain sight, but should not be opened until all the yarn has been wound into a ball.

Finally, take the ends of the yarn out of the room and close the door. When the time comes for gift-giving, give each member of the family the appropriate yarn and open the door on the multicolored Victorian web.

The *wonder ball* also involves yarn, and it is a marvelous idea for those who enjoy knitting. To make a wonder ball, just take a large ball of yarn and an assortment of small gifts. Unravel the yarn and rewind it carefully, hiding the tiny presents inside as you wind. In a good-sized ball of yarn, you should be able to conceal six or seven little gifts.

These presents will literally come to light in the next months as the recipient knits. If the knitting project happens to be a sweater for you, you will probably receive it in record time.

The *Christmas pie* is probably the most amusing of all Victorian gift-giving practices. It is nothing more than a large bowl filled with bran or other inexpensive grain, in which there have been hidden many little presents. The "pie" is brought out at the end of Christmas dinner, and the presents can be given in several ways.

Give everyone at the table a large spoon and let each person take a single dig into the bran, going around the table in turn; whatever emerges can be kept as a present. This gift-scooping continues until the pie has disappeared.

Or, attach colored string or ribbon to the presents and assign each diner a color. If you choose this method, you might take the trouble to wrap the presents as well, just to add to the deliciousness of the suspense as the ribbons are pulled from the pie.

Finally, a pie can be made for each member of the family, with a number of strings or ribbons sticking out of it. At the visible end of each ribbon, attach a tag announcing what time it can be pulled out of the pie. This method prolongs the fun, and it is an especially good choice if the last present is something very special indeed.

As Dickens takes pains to point out in *A Christmas Carol,* responsibility for giving at Christmas extends beyond the family; in the true spirit of giving, we should also share the joys of the holiday with those who may be less fortunate. Most of the Victorian crafts found in this chapter require inexpensive materials—the greatest investment is time. It would be very much in the Victorian spirit of Christmas to make arrangements to take these crafts and the materials they require into a home for children, for the aged, or a children's ward in a hospital.

Dickens, who was deeply concerned with such institutions, would no doubt approve.

From the great Victorian illustrator Arthur Rackham, a spirited game of Blindman's-Buff at the home of Scrooge's nephew Fred (1915). Courtesy of the Beinecke Rare Book and Manuscript Collection, Yale University.

Feasts and Revels

The Christmas Feast

Now that the rooms are decorated and gleaming–fragrant with pine and pomanders, the tree trimmed to perfection, the presents chosen and wrapped, and the fire prepared –the time has come for the entertainment.

For the Victorians, Christmas was a time for feasting. Usually, the evening began with libations and proceeded to dinner, followed by games. We will learn how to play some of the favorite games of Dickens' day at the end of this section, but first let us look at the Christmas feast and some of the traditions behind it.

From time immemorial, midwinter feasts have been held as an expression of faith in the plenty of the year to come, and also as a practical measure to make use of animals that could not live through the bitter winter months. Long before the rise of Christianity, these huge communal meals were traditional throughout Europe.

During the Middle Ages, the Christmas feast became the most important gathering of the year. In 878, Alfred the Great proclaimed that the full Twelve Days of Christmas should be celebrated throughout Britain, and his munificent gesture set the tone for the royalty who followed him.

Naturally, the seasonal feast was celebrated most lavishly by those who could best afford to celebrate it, and for several hundred years it was enjoyed mainly by royalty and by the nobility who served them. In 1248, though, King Henry III established the generous custom of giving food to the poor throughout the Twelve Days. He also extended the period of court feasting, in keeping with a growing tradition of royal extravagance. This led Richard II, in 1377, to give a dinner that employed 2,000 cooks to feed 10,000 people, who somehow managed to drink 200 large wooden casks (or "tuns") of wine.

Richard's carefree attitude toward the royal purse was one of the shortcomings that led to his downfall. But Henry V, the son of the man who overthrew Richard, was almost as spendthrift during the Christmas season. A chronicler described one of King Henry's Christmas gatherings as "a glutton mass celebration." This was not an exaggeration, if the partial list of what was eaten is correct. The entrees included venison, roast heron, capon, mutton, boar and beef. The rich and flesh-heavy menu accounts for the words of a French writer who complained, with a certain amount of envy some eighty years later, that the English "eat nothing but meat. The amount of bread one Frenchman eats in a day would be sufficient for four Englishmen."

By today's standards, the meat on the royal table was outrageously spicy. There were two reasons for the profusion of spices. First, since the preservation technology of the time was none too advanced, freshness was largely a matter of positive thinking, and spices helped to preserve the illusion. Second, spices suggested wealth. A common expression of the day was "as expensive as pepper."

The content of the dishes offered at Christmas under Henry V and his successors was only part of the story; the *way* they were served was equally strange from a modern perspective. Most of us today are not eager to be vividly reminded of the animal origins of some of our food. The medieval English, however, seemed to delight in making the main course look as much as possible like the beast from which it came.

Imagine the delicacy of an entire boar's head, served intact, with an apple in its mouth. It was brought to the table, preceded by a man holding a sword (supposedly the blade that proved fatal to the boar), accompanied by a minstrel or two singing "The Boar's Head Carol."

The tradition of the boar's head had its roots in England in a legend with scholarly overtones. Shortly after the establishment of Oxford University in the 12th century, a young student was wandering in the woods. Lost in thought, he failed to notice a large and ferocious boar charging directly at him until it was almost too late. Turning at the last possible moment, he hurled the only weapon he had on his person–a volume of Aristotle–into the mouth of the beast. The book choked the boar to death, saving the student's life, which may confirm many a later undergraduate's suspicions about the palatability of Aristotle. The young man had the boar hauled home in triumph and served as the centerpiece of the holiday meal. "The Boar's Head Carol" is traditional at Oxford during Christmastime even today.

A second medieval *pièce de résistance* that was still served occasionally in Dickens' time was roast peacock. This ornate dish was simply a peacock, skinned and roasted–but with a few refinements. First, it was skinned *before* it was plucked. Then, once the bird was roasted, the skin (feathers and all) was slipped back over it, and the tail was fanned out into its full glory.

As the peacock was brought to the table, usually by the highest-ranking ladies present, each man would lay his hands on it to vow a good deed in the year to come. In spite of all this attention, roast peacock was so dry and tasteless that many gravies were developed to moisten and tenderize it.

It would be a mistake, however, to think of meat as the sole Christmas delicacy savored by Henry V and his successors. Sugar was second only to spices in cost. Until sugarcane was cultivated on a grand scale in the Caribbean and in South America, it had to be brought all the way from Bengal, and its conspicuous use at banquet-time was a mark of royal wealth and security. Thus arose the elaborate and misnamed "subtleties," which were large molded or sculpted figures of sugar arranged into Nativity scenes complete with wise men, animals, holy family, crib and manger. These ephemeral artworks stood as table decorations throughout the feast until they were eaten as dessert at the very end of the meal.

The very end, by the way, sometimes came eight or nine hours after the lords and ladies sat down to table. Often there were as many as twelve main courses, and a certain amount of resting time had to be built into the program.

These culinary extravaganzas came to an abrupt halt under Oliver Cromwell when the Puritan Lord Protector outlawed the celebration of Christmas in 1652. For a decade, conspicuous consumption during the holidays was strictly forbidden; and even after Charles II was crowned in 1661, the excesses of the past never again became fashionable. In some stricter households, the prohibition continued in force even in Dickens' lifetime.

But those households were the exceptions. By the time Queen Victoria assumed the throne in 1837, Christmas dinner was the custom among most of the Englishmen who could afford it. In the north of the country, roast beef was the main course of preference, but in the south, most people agreed with Bob Cratchit that a succulent roast goose was the only proper centerpiece for the holiday table.

Of course, Christmas was a time for drinking as well as feasting, and we know that Dickens enjoyed an occasional glass of wine or champagne. At the time of his death in 1870, his wine cellar contained (and this is a very partial list): 209 bottles of sherry, 41 bottles of Madeira, 148 bottles of port, 474 bottles of red Bordeaux (but only 41 of red Burgundy) and 350 bottles of champagne!

Since most Victorian holiday gatherings began with libations, let us begin our recipes with directions for making some of these festive holiday drinks.

Christmas Drinks

When they were all tired of blind-man's buff, there was a great game at snap-dragon, and when fingers enough were burned with that, and all the raisins were gone, they sat down by the huge fire of blazing logs to a substantial supper, and a mighty bowl of wassail, something smaller than an ordinary wash-house copper, in which the hot apples were hissing and bubbling with a rich look, and a jolly sound, that were perfectly irresistible.

The Pickwick Papers

Wassail

Wassail was the festive center of the British Christmas for centuries. According to tradition, the drink dates back to the fifth century, when the British king, Vortigern, was served a bowl of hot spiced ale by a beautiful young Saxon woman named Rowena. As she handed the drink to him, she said "Waes-hael," which was the fifth-century equivalent of "Your health!" Either the words or the ale went straight to Vortigern's heart, because he and Rowena were married almost immediately.

As wassail became traditional over the centuries, the pomp surrounding it grew. In the great houses, it was served in an enormous bowl carried by a steward. All drank from the same bowl.

1 gallon brown ale
1 lb. soft brown sugar
1 or 2 cinnamon sticks
1 tsp. grated nutmeg
½ tsp. ground ginger
2 lemons, thinly sliced
1 bottle Madeira or sherry (25 oz.)
2 lbs. roasted apples

Put the cinnamon sticks and the sugar into a saucepan and add 2 pints of the ale. Stir and simmer until the sugar melts. Add the remaining ale, the sherry or Madeira, and the spices.

Bake the apples until soft. When they are ready, put the lemon slices into the bottom of a large bowl and pour the hot ale mixture over them. At the last moment before serving, drop the sizzling apples into the bowl. It is a drink worth singing about, and many carols have been written to celebrate it.

Love and joy come to you
And to you your wassail too,
And God bless you and send you
A happy new year.
And God send you a happy new year.

Eggnog

This delicious concoction of eggs, milk, sugar and alcohol is actually an American invention but, like the modern incarnation of Santa Claus, it crossed the ocean and found a congenial home in Britain. Of course, you can buy eggnog today in any market, but it is the slow addition of milk and cream to the liquor that makes the difference between an ordinary eggnog and a great one.

6 eggs
½ cup sugar
1½ cups bourbon
½ cup rum
½ cup brandy
Grated nutmeg
2 tsp. vanilla
3 cups heavy cream
1 pint milk
3 tbs. sugar

Separate the eggs and beat the yolks well, adding sugar gradually. Continue to beat as you add the liquor slowly. Then add the vanilla, stir it in, and allow the mixture to chill in the refrigerator for 1 hour. Then add the cream and milk in dollops, over a 24-hour period if possible.

When you want to serve the eggnog, beat the egg whites until stiffened. Fold half of them into the milk and alcohol mixture. Add 3 tablespoons of sugar to the remaining whites and make decorative peaks on top of each serving. Sprinkle with nutmeg.

Mulled Claret

In the chilly British winter, hot drinks have always been regarded as salutary. Here is one that will turn the most inexpensive red Bordeaux wine into a taste of old England.

1 bottle red Bordeaux (25 oz.)
20 oz. boiling water
1 wine glass of orange curaçao
1 wine glass of brandy
12 lumps of sugar
6 whole cloves
Nutmeg

Pour the wine into a saucepan and add the sugar and the cloves. Stir and simmer the mixture, not quite to a boil. Add the boiling water, and add the curaçao and brandy. Remove from the heat, let cool for several minutes, then pour the delightful mixture into cups or thick glasses and sprinkle with nutmeg.

Hot Bishop

"A merry Christmas, Bob!" said Scrooge, with an earnestness that could not be mistaken, as he clapped him on the back. "A merrier Christmas, Bob, my good fellow, than I have given you for many a year! I'll raise your salary, and endeavor to assist your struggling family, and we will discuss your affairs this very afternoon, over a Christmas bowl of smoking bishop..."

We'll never know exactly what Scrooge said to Bob Cratchit over that bowl of bishop–they had a lot to talk about–but we do know how to make this festive drink. Like wassail and mulled claret, it is served hot.

2 oranges
4 oz. sugar
1 bottle red wine (25 oz.)

Bake the oranges in a moderate oven until they turn pale brown. They should be sweet juice oranges with thin skins. Pierce each orange several times and put them into a large bowl. Pour in the red wine and add the sugar. Cover and let stand for at least 24 hours, and reheat before serving. Serve with a ladle to avoid spilling the oranges.

Charles Dickens' Very Own Punch

Brenda Marshall, in her *Charles Dickens Cookbook* (A.H. & A.W. Reed, Australia), quotes the following excerpt from one of Dickens' letters. In it, he gives the secret of his own homemade holiday punch, which sounds potent indeed. Ms. Marshall also makes the suggestion that the punch should be heated on top of the stove rather than in the oven, since it could conceivably ignite.

Peel into a very common basin (which may be broken in case of accident without damage to the owner's peace or pocket) the rinds of three lemons, cut very thin and with as little as possible of the white coating between the peel and the fruit, attached. Add a double handful of lump sugar, a pint of good old rum, and a large wine-glass of good old brandy–if it be not a large claret-glass, say two. Set this on fire, by filling a warm silver spoon with the spirit, lighting the contents at a wax taper, and pouring them gently in. Let it burn three or four minutes at least, stirring it from time to time. Then extinguish it by covering the basin with a tray, which will immediately put out the flame. Then squeeze in the juice of the three lemons, and add a quart of boiling water. Stir the whole thing well, cover it up for five minutes, and stir again.

At this crisis (having skimmed off the lemon pips with a spoon) you may taste. If not sweet enough, add sugar to your liking, but observe that it will be a little sweeter presently. Pour the whole into a jug, tie a leather or coarse cloth over the top, so as to exclude the air completely, and stand it in a hot oven ten minutes, or on a hot stove one quarter of an hour. Keep it until it comes to table in a warm place near a fire, but not too hot. If it be intended to stand three or four hours, take half the lemon peel out, or it will acquire a bitter taste. The same punch, allowed to grow cool by degrees, and then iced, is delicious.

The Victorian Christmas dinner, although not as heroically extravagant as its medieval predecessors, was still a heavy meal by today's standards. Two or three main courses were often served, followed by a bewildering variety of desserts. It was not uncommon for a family dinner on Christmas Eve or Christmas Day to last for two or three hours.

Individually, the following recipes should suit modern tastes quite well, although you may want to use only one or two at a meal, interspersing them with somewhat lighter fare. The effect will be heightened if the table is decorated in a Victorian fashion and candles are plentiful.

Braised Celery

2 bunches celery
1 can beef stock
3 tbs. butter

Cut the celery into 3-to-4-inch pieces and drop them into boiling water for about 8 minutes. Remove them, drain, and sauté in butter over a moderate flame until they are golden-brown. Add enough beef stock to cover, and simmer for 3 or 4 minutes. This is especially good as a side dish for poultry. 6 to 8 servings.

Spiced Peaches

This is another great appetizer for a dinner with a poultry main course, but it is equally appropriate for ham.

2½ lbs. fresh peaches
12 inches stick cinnamon
5 cups sugar
2 cups water
1 cup vinegar
2 tsp. whole cloves

Break cinnamon. In a 4-to-6-quart kettle combine sugar, water, vinegar and spices. Heat to boiling. Keep hot but not boiling. Wash peaches well; peel, halve and pit. Add peach halves to sugar syrup as soon as they are cut. Heat peaches in sugar syrup 5 minutes. Pack fruit and syrup into heated pint jars, leaving ½-inch headspace. Adjust lids. Process in boiling water bath 20 minutes. (Start timing when water returns to a boil.) Makes 3 pints.

The same recipe can be adapted for pears. Either makes a welcome Christmas gift.

Broiled Oysters on Toast

1 pint fresh oysters
½ stick melted butter
Worcestershire sauce
Salt, pepper, paprika

Shell, clean and drain the oysters. Place them in a shallow buttered pan and drizzle with a mixture of the remaining butter, Worcestershire sauce, salt, pepper and paprika. Broil until the oysters are plump. Serve on hot buttered toast and garnish with lemon wedges and parsley, if desired. 6 to 8 servings.

Fresh bread is welcome anywhere, especially on a festive occasion, and the fresh-baked loaf played an important nutritional and symbolic role at the Victorian table during the holiday season.

The Victorians frequently made a loaf of bread specifically *not* to eat; it was left on the table after Christmas dinner in the belief that it would guarantee plentiful bread throughout the year to come.

Homemade English Muffins

Here is a recipe that definitely *is* made to eat–in fact, the problem is eating too many of these tender muffins!

3 cups flour
1 tsp. salt
1 tsp. brown sugar
1/3 oz. fresh yeast
1 1/4 cups warm milk
1 beaten egg
2 tbs. melted butter

Sift the flour and the salt into a mixing bowl that has been greased lightly. Combine the yeast, sugar, and 3 or 4 tablespoons of the milk, mashing until creamy. Put the mixture someplace warm until it turns frothy; then stir the yeast mixture and the beaten egg into the flour. Add the melted butter and just enough warm milk to make a soft, workable dough.

Turn the dough out onto a large, well-floured board and knead until smooth and elastic. Place in a larger greased bowl, cover with a damp cloth, and let it stand in a warm spot until it doubles in size–about 1 hour. Re-flour the board and spill the dough out onto it, and punch the dough down. Divide it into 16 pieces and shape each into a circle about 3/4 of an inch thick. Cover the muffins with greased wax paper and let them rise for 20 to 30 minutes. Cook them gently, 5 or 6 at a time, on a greased griddle about 10 minutes on each side. Keep the muffins warm until you are ready to eat; then split them with a fork, and butter.

Christmas Wheat Wreaths

Here is a fancy bread that can be either eaten or hung on the wall as a decoration. This specific recipe comes from a wonderful book called *A Celebration of Christmas*, edited by Gillian Cooke (G.P. Putnam's Sons, New York).

4 cups all-purpose flour
1 tbs. salt
1/8 cup butter, melted
2 1/2 cups warm water
2 5/8 cups whole wheat flour
1 tbs. soft brown sugar
1 oz. fresh yeast

For the Topping:
1 egg, beaten
1 oz. sesame seeds

Sift the white flour and salt into a large bowl and add the whole wheat flour. Mix the sugar, yeast and 4 tablespoons of the water and leave until they dissolve. Stir this liquid and the melted butter into the flour, and add enough warm water to make a good dough. Knead the dough on a floured board for about 15 minutes, until it is elastic and lump-free. Place it in a large greased mixing bowl, cover with a damp cloth, and place in a warm spot to rise until it doubles in size.

Pour the dough onto the re-floured board and punch it down. Divide it in half. Return one piece to the mixing bowl. Grease a large baking sheet and the outside of a 6-inch cake pan. Take a piece of dough the size of an egg and divide the rest into 3 equal pieces. Roll these into long slender ropes about 28 inches long and braid them together. Put the braid on the baking sheet, around the greased cake pan. Wet the ends of the braid and join them together. Roll the egg-sized piece of dough, shape it into a bow and wet it to attach it to the loaf where the two ends of the braid have been joined. Cover with wax paper and allow to rise for half an hour in a warm place. Repeat the process with the other half of the dough.

When the wreaths are well-risen, paint them with beaten egg and sprinkle sesame seeds over them. Bake at 400°F for 10 minutes and then reduce heat to 375°F for another 25 to 30 minutes. When done, the loaves will sound hollow. If you bake both at once, reverse their positions in the oven midway through and give them a few extra minutes if necessary.

If you want to preserve one as a decoration, let it cool completely and then give it a coat of varnish.

Of course, appetizers and breads were nothing more than a preliminary fanfare to announce the impending arrival of the main course. The main course of Christmas dinner was something that many poorer families literally saved for all year long; and for the prosperous, it was a visible mark of their substance and wealth.

Roast Goose

There never was such a goose! Bob said he didn't believe there ever was such a goose cooked! Its tenderness and flavor, size and cheapness, were the themes of universal admiration.

A real-life counterpart of Bob Cratchit would almost certainly have purchased that magnificent goose through a "goose club," a Victorian forerunner of today's Christmas clubs, in which working-class people put aside a small amount of money each month toward purchase of the Christmas goose. Also, since the kitchen ovens of most people at the Cratchits' social level were too small to accommodate a goose, the bird was usually cooked for a small fee by the neighborhood baker.

1 10-lb. goose
Salt and freshly ground pepper
Apricot-walnut stuffing

If frozen, thaw goose by placing it in its wrapper in a sink of cold water for 4 or 5 hours. (Thawing by this method restores the goose to full freshness.) Drain and dry with paper towels. Sprinkle cavity with salt and pepper. Loosely stuff with apricot-walnut stuffing. Roast at 400° F for 1 hour. Lower to 325° F and continue roasting 1½-to-2 hours. When cooked, the thigh, if pricked with a fork, should run beige juice, not pink. There is no need to baste a goose during roasting, but you should siphon off the drippings every half hour. Let goose rest for 30 minutes. 8 to 10 servings.

Apricot-Walnut Stuffing

1 cup canned apricots, drained
¼ cup melted butter
6 cups cubed day-old bread
1 cup chopped walnuts
½ cup golden raisins
1 tsp. salt
½ tsp. poultry seasoning
¼ tsp. freshly ground pepper

Dice apricots. In a bowl, pour melted butter over bread cubes. Combine with apricots and remaining ingredients. Toss lightly to mix well. Makes enough stuffing for a 10-to-12-pound goose.

Turkey Stuffing and Bread Sauce

The turkey was imported into Europe from the New World in the late 1500s. By 1843, when Dickens wrote *A Christmas Carol*, turkeys were still a delicacy. Scrooge could afford to buy one for the Cratchits, but Cratchit himself had to be satisfied with goose—even though turkeys were being raised by the thousands outside London and driven into the city daily during the Christmas holidays.

Any American cookbook has at least one good recipe for roasting a turkey, but here are two British accompaniments that will give this American bird a truly Dickensian flavor.

Stuffing

1 lb. fresh crushed bread crumbs
½ lb. soft butter
1 tsp. diced celery
2 pinches cayenne pepper
Salt, black pepper to taste
¼ pint fresh cream
3 pints fresh oysters, shelled, cleaned and drained (reserve liquid)

Mix into the bread crumbs the soft butter, diced celery, cayenne, salt, black pepper and cream. When mixed well, add the oysters and remix. When making gravy from the pan drippings, add a cupful of the reserved oyster liquid. 8 to 10 servings.

Bread Sauce

This is an alternative to the oyster-based gravy, and not a suggested addition.

1 onion
4-6 whole cloves
1 bay leaf
1½ cups milk
2 cups white bread crumbs
Salt
Black pepper

Peel the onion and stud it with the cloves, then heat it slowly with the milk and bay leaf until it boils. Remove the pan from heat and let it cool for about 30 minutes.

Discard the onion, cloves and bay leaf. Stir the bread crumbs into the milk and heat, stirring until the mixture boils and the sauce is smooth and thick. Season with salt and pepper. Serve hot with the turkey. 8 to 10 servings.

Roast Beef with Yorkshire Pudding

This is the authentic, noble, British "sir loin" that is still the favored Christmas entree in many parts of the British Isles. This recipe calls for the beef to be slightly rarer than is the usual English custom; if you prefer it well-done, you can always give it an extra 5 minutes per pound. 8 to 10 servings.

For the Roast

1 8-lb. standing rib roast
½ stick soft butter
Salt
Pepper, freshly ground

Place roast, fat side up, on a rack in a shallow roasting pan. Brush with softened butter and season with salt and pepper. Roast, uncovered, at 325°F until a meat thermometer inserted in the center of the meat registers 140°F (3-3¼ hours). Remove meat from pan and cover to keep warm. Reserve ¼ cup of pan drippings and increase oven setting to 400°F.

For the Pudding

2 cups milk
4 eggs
2 cups all-purpose flour
1 tsp. salt

Mix flour and salt in mixing bowl. Combine milk and eggs, add to flour, and beat until smooth. Pour half the reserved pan drippings into each of two 9x9x2-inch baking pans, brushing the sides. Pour half the batter into each pan and bake at 400°F for 30 minutes.

"In Half a Minute Mrs. Cratchit Entered," by Arthur Rackham (1915). Courtesy of the Arthur Rackham Collection, Rare Book and Manuscript Library, Columbia University.

Plum Pudding with Sauce

In half a minute Mrs. Cratchit entered–flushed, but smiling proudly –with the pudding, like a speckled cannon-ball, so hard and firm, blazing in half of half-a-quartern of ignited brandy, and bedight with Christmas holly stuck into the top.

Oh, a wonderful pudding! Bob Cratchit said, and calmly too, that he regarded it as the greatest success achieved by Mrs. Cratchit since their marriage. Mrs. Cratchit said, that now the weight was off her mind, she would confess she had had her doubts about the quantity of flour.

To Americans, it may seem strange that a pudding even *contains* flour; but it is positively paradoxical that a plum pudding, in addition to containing flour, contains not a bit of plum.

In fact, the "plum" in the name may be a corruption of "plumb," which, several centuries ago, meant "to swell," as the raisins in a plum pudding do during the cooking process. At any rate, it is believed that the dish was first named in a 1791 cookbook, and "plumb pudding" is what it was then called.

Plum pudding has an evolutionary history that would be the envy of many biological species. It probably began in medieval times as "frumenty," an unappetizing-sounding mess of boiled wheat and grain to which meat was often added. For centuries, the meat grew in importance until it became the prime ingredient. Today, however, it remains only in vestigial form as a cup of ground suet that acts as shortening.

Plum pudding is often served with a topping of ignited brandy.

The simplified modern recipe that follows is taken from Sunny O'Neil's charming book, *The Gift of Christmas Past* (American Association for State and Local History, Nashville, Tennessee).

1 cup ground suet
1 cup raisins
2 cups dry bread crumbs
½ cup chopped nuts
1 cup sugar
½ cup milk
1 beaten egg
½ tsp. soda
1 tsp. cinnamon
½ tsp. each ground cloves, allspice, salt
*Coins (optional)**

Mix all ingredients well and pour the batter into a greased pudding mold or a greased tin can. If you are using a can, grease it well and fill about ⅔ full.

Cover with a lid or with foil. Steam for 2 hours in boiling water. Unmold, pour cognac over it, and ignite. Serve with sauce. 6 to 8 servings.

**In Dickens' day, it was customary to scatter silver coins into the pudding. These supposedly brought luck to those who bit down on them. We live in more dental-conscious times, but the recipe would be incomplete if it failed to acknowledge this tradition.*

The Sauce

2 egg yolks
1 cup confectioners' sugar
½ cup whipping cream
Vanilla extract
Rum or sherry (optional)

Beat the egg yolks, adding the sugar and continuing to beat until smooth. Whip the cream and fold it in. Then add vanilla and, if you wish, rum or sherry.

Mince Pie

The venerable mince pie is an ancient recipe. Like plum pudding, it has gone through several stages of development and once contained a substantial amount of meat. The poet Robert Herrick celebrated it in these lines that suggest how highly it was valued:

Come guard the Christmas pie
That the thief, though ne'er so sly,
With his flesh-hooks don't come nigh
to catch it.

½ cup seeded raisins
½ cup sultana raisins
¼ cup currants
8 oz. cooking apples, chopped
1 tbs. ground almonds
½ cup packed brown sugar
1 tbs. shredded suet
2 tsp. mixed spices: equal amounts of cinnamon, allspice, cloves, mace
Juice and grated peel of 1 lemon
1 wine glass of cognac (optional)

Preheat oven to 400° F.
Wash and dry currants and raisins and mince with the chopped apples. Add the almonds, sugar, suet, spices, lemon juice and peel. Add the brandy, if you wish. Spoon into a pie shell and cover with top crust. Bake for 35-40 minutes, until crust is golden.

Apple Roly Poly

Biscuit or pie dough
Rind of ½ lemon, grated
Whipped cream
4 green apples, chopped fine
Cinnamon, allspice
½ cup sugar

Preheat oven to 350° F.
Roll the pastry into 8 thin circles, each about 5 inches in diameter. Lift carefully and place on a well-greased cookie sheet.

Spoon the chopped apples into the center of each circle of dough. Add sugar, cinnamon, allspice and lemon rind (use lemon rind sparingly!).

Wet the edges of the dough and fold in half, omelette-fashion. Crimp the edges to seal. Dust sugar over dough, and bake for about 25-30 minutes, until golden-brown. Serve warm with whipped cream.

Berry Trifle with Custard Sauce

A "trifle" is a traditional English dessert usually involving fruit and sponge cake of some kind. Unlike the ornate "subtleties" mentioned earlier, trifles actually are unassuming desserts, and easy to prepare–but delicious.

1 sponge cake, thinly sliced
1 cup milk
Lemon extract
Vanilla
2 cups stewed raspberries, strawberries or blackberries

Line a glass serving bowl with slices of sponge cake. Flavor the milk with sugar and vanilla until it suits your taste. Add lemon extract for a hint of tartness and fragrance. Sprinkle the sweetened milk over the cake to moisten it, and then spoon the stewed berries over the cake. Put the dish into the refrigerator to chill 1 or 2 hours. Before serving, pour custard sauce over it. 6 to 8 servings.

Custard Sauce

4 egg yolks
1 cup sugar
2 cups milk

Beat the yolks as they heat in the top of a double boiler. Stir in the milk and sugar and cook, stirring briskly, until thick and golden. Chill before serving.

The indispensable plum pudding, cheesecloth and all, by Robert Seymour (1836). Courtesy of the New York Public Library Picture Collection.

The After-Dinner Revels

"This," said Mr. Pickwick, looking round him, "this is, indeed, comfort."
"Our invariable custom," replied Mr. Wardle. "Everybody sits down with us on Christmas eve, as you see them now–servants and all; and here we wait till the clock strikes twelve, to usher Christmas in, and while the time away with forfeits and old stories."

The Pickwick Papers

When the crumbs were cleaned from the last plate and the setting had been cleared away, the Victorian family and guests adjourned to the sitting room, and the second phase of the festivities began. Often a good deal of preparation had gone into what followed.

Dickens, for example, was a skillful amateur magician, and Christmas gatherings at his home and those of his friends gave him the excuse he had yearned for all year to mystify his acquaintances with disappearing pennies and multicolored scarves pulled from thin air. His efforts were appreciated. One of his friends, Jane Welsh Carlyle, wrote in a letter to her family: "Only think of that excellent Dickens playing the *conjuror* for a whole hour–the *best* conjuror I ever saw!"

Some gatherings were highlighted by theatrical presentations in which all members of the family played a part. Most middle- and upper-class Victorian homes had a piano or spinet, and people far too respectable ever to sing in public took advantage of the holiday to entertain their friends with Christmas songs and other favorites.

But for many–especially the young–games were the climax of the Christmas Eve celebration. Some of the games the Victorians played have come down to us unchanged: Dickens' favorite, Charades, for example, and Blindman's Buff. Some have taken on a distinctly exotic tinge with time. The game of Snap-dragon, played in a dark room, consisted of snatching raisins or currants from burning brandy and popping them into the mouth without (one hoped) getting burned. The flaming spirits were said to cast an eerie, flickering glow on the faces of the players. Another game involved acting out, in pantomime, a famous incident from literature or history. An American visitor remembered, as the high point of his sojourn in London, seeing Dickens, with a black handkerchief on his head and a fire shovel to represent an axe, joining with the novelist Wilkie Collins to enact the execution of Mary, Queen of Scots.

Today, few people play many of the games that Dickens and his contemporaries so enjoyed, even though they would enliven practically any gathering. Here are five parlor games that you and your family can try this Christmas.

The Memory Game

The guests sit in a circle, and the host or hostess speaks a single word. The person seated immediately to the left must repeat the first word and add one of his or her own, and the next person must remember both preceding words and add a third, and so on around the circle. Anyone who fails to repeat correctly the ever-lengthening chain of words is eliminated, and thus the circle grows smaller as the list grows longer. The last person is the winner.

This game is of special interest to lovers of Dickens' work, because it led to the first and only time Dickens revealed what was to him the darkest and most shameful part of his life. One of the keys to success in the game was using a word with special private meaning, making it unlikely that a player would forget his or her own word. During a game on one Christmas Eve, Dickens, who was enormously competitive, chose the word "Warren's." When the game ended, he retired from the room, clearly disturbed about something; later, in a letter, he explained to a friend that Warren's was the name of the blacking factory where he had been sent to work as a boy.

Shadow Buff

This is a variation on Blindman's Buff, in which the person who is "it" must identify others at the party by their shadows. It can be played in two ways. First, a sheet can be hung from floor to ceiling in the center of the room, and a strong light cast upon it. The person who is "it" stands on one side and the guest standing between the light and the sheet on the other side, casts a shadow. If no sheet is available, "it" can face a wall with his back to the person whose shadow is being cast on the wall.

Either way, this game is even more challenging and authentic when the source of light is a flickering candle.

Literary Salad

There are few games more Victorian in concept than this one. Pieces of colored paper are cut to resemble leaves of lettuce, slices of tomato, and other vegetables. On each is written a literary quotation or famous words from history. The papers are then jumbled together into a salad bowl, and each player draws one in turn. If the player cannot correctly attribute the words to the correct authors, he must pay a forfeit by doing something silly, such as kissing his own shadow or crawling around the room twice. Thinking up forfeits is almost as much fun as playing the game.

The Minister's Cat

Another circle game, The Minister's Cat, tests the impromptu verbal skills of the guests. The host or hostess begins by saying something like "the minister's cat is an awful cat." The turn passes left, with every member of the circle supplying an appropriate word beginning with the letter "A" to describe the cat. When the host's turn comes round again, he suggests a "B" word–for example, "the minister's cat is a brown cat," and the game proceeds on through the alphabet. Any player who cannot think of a word within five seconds is eliminated, and the last surviving player wins.

This game has many variations. One of them uses the catchline, "with my pudding, I ate a...," and the game is played in the same way, beginning with the letter "A."

Poker and Tongs

Children especially love this extremely noisy game, which should probably not be played in apartment houses, at least not late at night. As in the familiar game of Hot-and-Cold, the person who is "it" must hunt for something the location of which is known to everyone else in the room. All the other guests are given spoons, fireplace tools–objects that will produce a substantial amount of noise when beaten together. When "it" is far from the hidden treasure, the other players bang their noise-makers together slowly and quietly; as discovery nears, the noise gets faster and louder.

With the holiday dinner behind them and the sounds of Poker and Tongs echoing in their ears, the Victorian family went to bed at the stroke of midnight, pleased that they had joined together to prepare the house for their celebration, decorated the tree, shared the meal, and enjoyed games, friends and children.

They had also joined their voices in song. Those songs, and the traditions behind them, are the subject of the next section.

"Fred's Wife, With Children," by Arthur Rackham (1915). Courtesy of the Arthur Rackham Collection, Rare Book and Manuscript Library, Columbia University.

Sing a Song of Christmas: Christmas Carols and the Caroling Tradition

Deck the halls with boughs of holly,
Fa la la la la la la la la.
'Tis the season to be jolly,
Fa la la la la la la la la.

Christmas is the most musical of holidays. Why is it the occasion for so much singing? Why have so many songs–not only purely religious songs, but secular songs as well–been written to celebrate this singularly musical season?

The answer may lie within the Gospel of St. Luke. In chapter two, Luke says that the shepherds in the fields were amazed when an angel came to them and told them of the birth of Jesus. Luke recounts:

And suddenly there was with the angel a multitude of the heavenly host praising God and saying,
Glory to God in the highest, and on earth peace, good will to men.

Although, in most translations, Luke uses the word "saying" rather than "singing," these words are so musical that we come away with the impression that the heavenly host sang. And, in fact, those very words, in various translations, have been set to music countless times in the two millenia since the Gospel of St. Luke was written.

It is certain that music played an important part in the earliest celebrations of Christmas. We are told that Christmas songs were sung in the churches of Rome as early as 129 A.D., and St. Jerome mentions carols in the fifth century. By the 14th century, Christmas songs were being sung between the acts of the miracle and mystery plays performed outside the churches to tell the stories of the Bible to those who could not read.

The origins of the earliest carols are often extremely difficult to trace. "The First Noel," for example, may be German, French or English; words in all three languages date from almost four hundred years ago. The problem of pinning down the origins of carols is compounded by the fact that they traveled more widely and more swiftly than any other popular musical form; "Silent Night," for example, was translated into at least six European languages within thirty years of its composition in 1818.

In England, caroling has always been an indispensable and joyous part of the holiday. Many of the earliest of the English carols were preserved in a diary or "commonplace book" that was kept by a grocer's apprentice named Richard Hill between the years 1500 and 1536. Hill wrote down things that were of special interest to him–and, fortunately for us, he was very interested in carols. In a storybook instance of literary luck, his volume was discovered wedged behind an old bookcase in 1850. Thanks to this piece of good fortune and Richard Hill's enthusiasm, we have the earliest of all surviving English secular carols, "The Boar's Head Carol" mentioned in section four, as well as several others that would have been lost to us forever.

British caroling was inextricably linked with wassailing. On Christmas Eve, groups of children and adults would go from house

to house singing carols and receiving cups of steaming hot wassail or food in return, in keeping with the custom that none who knocked on the door could be turned away during the Twelve Days of Christmas. Some of the wassailing songs were charmingly direct in stating the carolers' ulterior motive:

Good Master and good Mistress,
While you're sitting by the fire,
Pray think of us poor children
Who are wandering in the mire.

Some carols, such as "The First Noel," retold biblical stories while others–especially in England–were essentially secular in nature. "Deck the Halls," for example, never mentions the birth of Jesus, concentrating instead on older traditions such as the Yule log and the indoor display of greenery. "Good King Wenceslaus," while certainly Christian in spirit, takes as its hero a 10th-century king (or duke) of Bohemia noted for his charity toward the poor. One of the verses of this beautiful carol directly addresses the issue raised by Dickens in *A Christmas Carol,* the responsibility of the well-off to aid their less fortunate brethren at Christmastime:

Therefore Christian men, be sure,
Wealth or rank possessing,
Ye who now will bless the poor,
Will yourselves find blessing.

Despite the long tradition of caroling in England, by Dickens' time it was a dying custom. Oliver Cromwell banned carols along with all other observances of the holiday, and the custom never revived with the full vitality it had enjoyed prior to the time the Puritans were in power. The custom continued to wane in the 17th and 18th centuries, despite the efforts of British printers who circulated carols on cheap, oversized pieces of paper called "broadsides," which usually sold for a penny.

By 1830, in the larger cities, caroling had degenerated into a sort of advanced begging technique employed seasonally by the more musically inclined poor. The boy who annoys Scrooge by beginning "God Rest Ye Merry, Gentlemen" (he sings "bless" rather than "rest") is not singing for the joy of his listeners; he hopes to receive money.

By 1833, "God Rest Ye Merry, Gentlemen"–that is the proper punctuation, by the way; the title actually means "God keep you merry, gentlemen"–was known in the cities as "the" carol, as if it were the only one in existence. When William Sandys began in that year to compile his volume of *Ancient and Modern Christmas Carols,* he had to travel to the midlands and further north to collect his songs, since the caroling tradition had virtually disappeared from London.

The Victorians rediscovered the special joy of these unique songs and reinstated the carol in a place of honor during the Christmas celebration. Dickens helped by calling his first Christmas book *A Christmas Carol,* and musicians and poets alike joined forces to track down and publish the old songs. The most important of all the Victorian collections, *Christmas Carols Old and New,* was published in 1871.

As you sing your favorite carols this year (and some of them are sure to be among the ones that follow), you might sing one in honor of those anonymous Victorian ladies and gentlemen whose musical skill and Christmas spirit helped to revive this most joyous and harmonious of holiday customs.

Silent Night

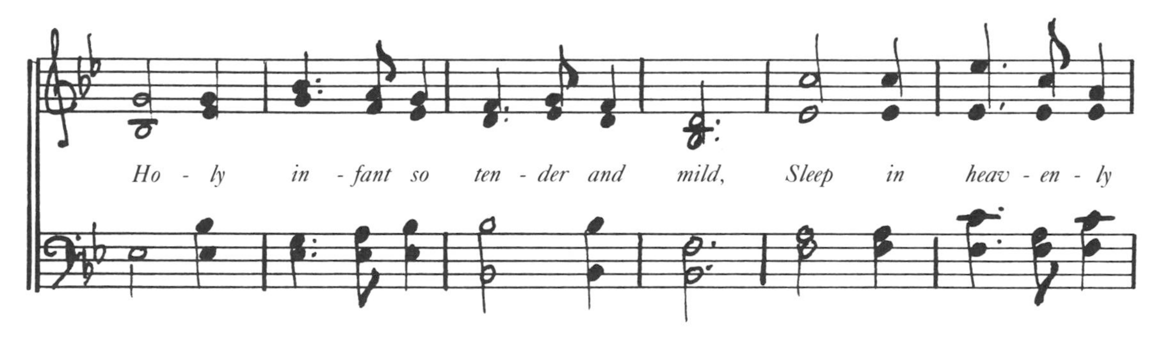

Probably the most popular carol in the world, "Silent Night," was written in 1818 in a small Austrian town. Its authors were the village priest, Father Joseph Mohr, and his organist, Franz Gruber.

On the afternoon of Christmas Eve in that year, Father Mohr noticed that mice had damaged the church organ, making it unplayable. Desperate for something that could be sung without organ accompaniment, he wrote the words (in German, of course) to "Silent Night" and hurried through the snow to the house of his friend, Herr Gruber. Gruber wrote the music in just a few hours, and at midnight mass that evening the two of them sang it, joined by two women, and accompanied by Herr Gruber's Spanish guitar.

Silent night, holy night,
Shepherds quake at the sight.
Glories stream from heaven afar,
Heav'nly hosts sing Alleluia;
Christ the Savior is born;
Christ the Savior is born.

Silent night, holy night,
Son of God, love's pure light.
Radiant beams from Thy holy face,
With the dawn of redeeming grace,
Jesus, Lord, at Thy birth;
Jesus, Lord, at Thy birth.

Joy to the World

This jubilant carol is the best-known work of Isaac Watts, one of the most prolific of carol and hymn writers (although his total of 600 songs of celebration looks paltry next to Charles Wesley's more than 6,500). Watts was the son of a minister, and when he complained, at the age of fifteen, that the music being sung in church was uninspiring, his father challenged him to write something better. He did. Later in his life, he retired from the clergy because of ill health and devoted himself solely to writing hymns and carols.

"Joy to the World" is based on the 98th Psalm. The music to which the words are sung is adapted from Handel's "Messiah."

Joy to the world! the Savior reigns:
Let men their songs employ,
While fields and floods, rocks, hills and plains
Repeat the sounding joy, repeat the sounding joy,
Repeat, repeat the sounding joy.

He rules the world with truth and grace,
And makes the nations prove
The glories of His righteousness
And wonders of His love, and wonders of His love,
And wonders, wonders of His love.

Hark! The Herald Angels Sing

The words to this popular carol were written in 1730 by Charles Wesley. Wesley, whose brother, John, was the founder of the Methodist Church, was probably the most prolific hymn-writer of all time. He wrote more than 6,500 hymns and carols, of which this is the most familiar.

Wesley's actual opening line was: "Hark! How all the welkin rings." (Now obscure, "welkin" means "sky.") The words were changed thirty years later by another hymn-writer, the Reverend Martin Madan. They were not set to the music we know until 1855, when Dr. W.H. Cummings adapted a tune by Mendelssohn to fit them. Ironically, Mendelssohn had said earlier of the melody: "I am sure that this piece will never do for sacred words." He felt that something martial would be more appropriate.

Christ by highest heav'n adored;
Christ the everlasting Lord!
Late in time behold Him come,
Offspring of a Virgin's womb.
Veiled in flesh the Godhead see;
Hail the incarnate Deity.
Pleased as man with man to dwell,
Jesus, our Emmanuel!

Deck the Halls

Another old British carol, "Deck the Halls," is known the world over. The melody is Welsh, and Mozart once used it, virtually unchanged, in a violin sonata.

See the blazing Yule before us,
Fa la la la la la la la la.
Strike the harp and join the chorus,
Fa la la la la la la la la.
Follow me in merry measure,
Fa la la la la la la la la.
While I tell of Yuletide treasure,
Fa la la la la la la la la.

God Rest Ye Merry, Gentlemen

One of the most popular of all carols and among the merriest, in spite of the fact that it is set in a minor key, "God Rest Ye Merry, Gentlemen" is the carol most closely associated with Dickens. This is not only because it is briefly mentioned in *A Chistmas Carol*, but also because it conjures up Dickens' world of merry, good-hearted fellowship, crackling fires and hot mulled wine.

In Bethlehem, in Israel, this blessed Babe was born,
And laid within a manger upon this blessed morn;
The which His Mother Mary did nothing take in scorn.

Chorus
O tidings of comfort and joy, comfort and joy!
O tidings of comfort and joy!

From God our heav'nly Father, a blessed angel came;
And unto certain shepherds brought tidings of the same;
How that in Bethlehem was born the Son of God by name.

Chorus
O tidings of comfort and joy, comfort and joy!
O tidings of comfort and joy!

(Title)

A Christmas Carol
In Prose;
Being a Ghost Story of Christmas.
By Charles Dickens

The Illustrations by John Leech

Chapman and Hall 186 Strand
MDCCCXLIII.

(My own, and only MS of the Book)
Charles Dickens

A Christmas Carol: Dickens' Tale in Full

The title page from Dickens' own manuscript of "A Christmas Carol" (1843). By permission of The Pierpont Morgan Library, New York.

Preface

I have endeavoured in this Ghostly little book, to raise the Ghost of an Idea, which shall not put my readers out of humour with themselves, with each other, with the season, or with me. May it haunt their house pleasantly, and no one wish to lay it.

Their faithful Friend and Servant,
C. D.

December 1843.

Table of Contents

Stave I.

Marley's Ghost.

Marley was dead: to begin with. There is no doubt whatever, about that. The register of his burial was signed by the clergyman, the clerk, the undertaker, and the chief mourner. Scrooge signed it: and Scrooge's name was good upon 'Change, for anything he chose to put his hand to. Old Marley was as dead as a door-nail.

Mind! I don't mean to say that I know, of my own knowledge, what there is particularly dead about a door-nail. I might have been inclined, myself, to regard a coffin-nail as the deadest piece of Ironmongery in the trade. But the wisdom of our ancestors is in the simile; and my unhallowed hands shall not disturb it, or the country's done for. You will therefore permit me to repeat, emphatically, that Marley was as dead as a door-nail.

Scrooge knew he was dead? Of course he did. How could it be otherwise? Scrooge and he were partners for I don't know how many years. Scrooge was his sole executor, his sole administrator, his sole assign, his sole residuary legatee, his sole friend and sole mourner. And even Scrooge was not so dreadfully cut up by the sad event, but that he was an excellent man of business on the very day of the funeral, and solemnized it with an undoubted bargain.

The mention of Marley's funeral brings me back to the point I started from. There is no doubt that Marley was dead. This must be distinctly understood, or nothing wonderful can come of the story I am going to relate. If we were not perfectly convinced that Hamlet's Father died before the play began, there would be nothing more remarkable in his taking a stroll at night, in an easterly wind, upon his own ramparts, than there would be in any other middle-aged gentleman rashly turning out after dark in a breezy spot — say Saint Paul's churchyard for instance — literally to astonish his son's weak mind.

[illegible]

Scrooge never painted out old Marley's name. There it

Stave 

Marley's Ghost

Marley was dead: to begin with. There is no doubt whatever about that. The register of his burial was signed by the clergyman, the clerk, the undertaker, and the chief mourner. Scrooge signed it: and Scrooge's name was good upon 'Change, for anything he chose to put his hand to. Old Marley was as dead as a door-nail.

Mind! I don't mean to say that I know, of my own knowledge, what there is particularly dead about a door-nail. I might have been inclined, myself, to regard a coffin-nail as the deadest piece of ironmongery in the trade. But the wisdom of our ancestors is in the simile; and my unhallowed hands shall not disturb it, or the Country's done for. You will therefore permit me to repeat, emphatically, that Marley was as dead as a door-nail.

Scrooge knew he was dead? Of course he did. How could it be otherwise? Scrooge and he were partners for I don't know how many years. Scrooge was his sole executor, his sole administrator, his sole assign, his sole residuary legatee, his sole friend and sole mourner. And even Scrooge was not so dreadfully cut up by the sad event, but that he was an excellent man of business on the very day of the funeral, and solemnised it with an undoubted bargain.

The mention of Marley's funeral brings me back to the point I started from. There is no doubt that Marley was dead. This must be distinctly understood, or nothing wonderful can come of the story I am going to relate. If we were not perfectly convinced that Hamlet's Father died before the play began, there would be nothing more remarkable in his taking a stroll at night, in an easterly wind, upon his own ramparts, than there would be in any other middle-aged gentleman rashly turning out after dark in a

"Marley was dead…" Page one of Dickens' manuscript of "A Christmas Carol" (1843). By permission of The Pierpont Morgan Library, New York.

breezy spot–say Saint Paul's Churchyard for instance–literally to astonish his son's weak mind.

Scrooge never painted out Old Marley's name. There it stood, years afterwards, above the warehouse door: Scrooge and Marley. The firm was known as Scrooge and Marley. Sometimes people new to the business called Scrooge Scrooge, and sometimes Marley, but he answered to both names: it was all the same to him.

Oh! but he was a tight-fisted hand at the grindstone, Scrooge! a squeezing, wrenching, grasping, scraping, clutching, covetous old sinner! Hard and sharp as flint, from which no steel had ever struck out generous fire; secret, and self-contained, and solitary as an oyster. The cold within him froze his old features, nipped his pointed nose, shrivelled his cheek, stiffened his gait; made his eyes red, his thin lips blue; and spoke out shrewdly in his grating voice. A frosty rime was on his head, and on his eyebrows, and his wiry chin. He carried his own low temperature always about with him; he iced his office in the dog-days; and didn't thaw it one degree at Christmas.

External heat and cold had little influence on Scrooge. No warmth could warm, nor wintry weather chill him. No wind that blew was bitterer than he, no falling snow was more intent upon its purpose, no pelting rain less open to entreaty. Foul weather didn't know where to have him. The heaviest rain, and snow, and hail, and sleet, could boast of the advantage over him in only one respect. They often "came down" handsomely, and Scrooge never did.

Nobody ever stopped him in the street to say, with gladsome looks, "My dear Scrooge, how are you? when will you come to see me?" No beggars implored him to bestow a trifle, no children asked him what it was o'clock, no man or woman ever once in all his life inquired the way to such and such a place, of Scrooge. Even the blindmen's dogs appeared to know him; and when they saw him coming on, would tug their owners into doorways and up courts; and then would wag their tails as though they said, "no eye at all is better than an evil eye, dark master!"

But what did Scrooge care? It was the very thing he liked. To edge his way along the crowded paths of life, warning all human sympathy to keep its distance, was what the knowing ones call "nuts" to Scrooge.

Once upon a time–of all the good days in the year, on Christmas Eve–old Scrooge sat busy in his counting-house. It was cold, bleak, biting weather: foggy withal: and he could hear the people in the court outside, go wheezing up and down, beating their hands upon their breasts, and stamping their feet upon the pavement-stones to warm them. The city clocks had only just gone three, but it was quite dark already: it had not been light all day: and candles were flaring in the windows of the neighbouring offices, like ruddy smears upon the palpable brown air. The fog came pouring in at every chink and keyhole, and was so dense without, that although the court was of the narrowest, the houses opposite were mere phantoms. To see the dingy cloud come drooping down, obscuring everything, one might have thought that Nature lived hard by, and was brewing on a large scale.

The door of Scrooge's counting-house was open that he might keep his eye upon his clerk, who in a dismal little cell beyond, a sort of tank, was copying letters. Scrooge had a very small fire, but the clerk's fire was so very much smaller that it looked like one coal. But he couldn't replenish it, for Scrooge kept the coal-box in his own room; and so surely as the clerk came in with the shovel, the master predicted that it would be necessary for them to part. Wherefore the clerk put on his white comforter, and tried to warm himself at the candle; in which effort, not being a man of a strong imagination, he failed.

"A merry Christmas, uncle! God save you!" cried a cheerful voice. It was the voice of Scrooge's nephew, who came upon him so quickly that this was the first intimation he had of his approach.

"Bah!" said Scrooge, "Humbug!"

He had so heated himself with rapid walking in the fog and frost, this nephew of Scrooge's, that he was all in a glow; his face was ruddy and handsome; his eyes sparkled, and his breath smoked again.

"Christmas a humbug, uncle!" said Scrooge's nephew. "You don't mean that, I am sure?"

"I do," said Scrooge. "Merry Christmas! What right have you to be merry? what reason have you to be merry? You're poor enough."

"Come, then," returned the nephew gaily. "What right have you to be dismal? what reason have you to be morose? You're rich enough."

Scrooge having no better answer ready on the spur of the moment, said, "Bah!" again; and followed it up with "Humbug."

"Don't be cross, uncle," said the nephew.

"What else can I be" returned the uncle, "when I live in such a world of fools as this? Merry Christmas! Out upon merry Christmas! What's Christmas time to you but a time for paying bills without money; a time for finding yourself a year older, and not an hour richer; a time for balancing your books and having every item in 'em through a round dozen of months presented dead against you? If I could work my will," said Scrooge, indignantly, "every idiot who goes about with 'Merry Christmas,' on his lips, should be boiled with his own pudding, and buried with a stake of holly through his heart. He should!"

"Uncle!" pleaded the nephew.

"Nephew!" returned the uncle, sternly, "keep Christmas in your own way, and let me keep it in mine."

"Keep it!" repeated Scrooge's nephew. "But you don't keep it."

"Let me leave it alone, then," said Scrooge. "Much good may it do you! Much good it has ever done you!"

"There are many things from which I might have derived good, by which I have not profited, I dare say," returned the nephew: "Christmas among the rest. But I am sure I have always thought of Christmas time, when it has come round–apart from the veneration due to its sacred name and origin, if anything belonging to it can be apart from that–as a good time: a kind, forgiving, charitable, pleasant time: the only time I know of, in the long calendar of the year, when men and women seem by one consent to open their shut-up hearts freely, and to think of people below them as if they really were fellow-passengers to the grave, and not another race of creatures bound on other journeys. And therefore, uncle, though it has never put a scrap of gold or silver in my pocket, I believe that it *has* done me good, and *will* do me good; and I say, God bless it!"

The clerk in the tank involuntarily applauded: becoming immediately sensible of the impropriety, he poked the fire, and extinguished the last frail spark for ever.

"Let me hear another sound from *you*" said Scrooge, "and you'll keep your Christmas by losing your situation. You're quite a powerful speaker, sir," he added, turning to his nephew. "I wonder you don't go into Parliament."

"Don't be angry, uncle. Come! Dine with us to-morrow."

Scrooge said that he would see him—yes, indeed he did. He went the whole length of the expression, and said that he would see him in that extremity first.

"But why?" cried Scrooge's nephew. "Why?"

"Why did you get married?" said Scrooge.

"Because I fell in love."

"Because you fell in love!" growled Scrooge, as if that were the only one thing in the world more ridiculous than a merry Christmas. "Good afternoon!"

"Nay, uncle, but you never came to see me before that happened. Why give it as a reason for not coming now?"

"Good afternoon," said Scrooge.

"I want nothing from you; I ask nothing of you; why cannot we be friends?"

"Good afternoon," said Scrooge.

"I am sorry, with all my heart, to find you so resolute. We have never had any quarrel, to which I have been a party. But I have made the trial in homage to Christmas, and I'll keep my Christmas humour to the last. So A Merry Christmas, uncle!"

"Good afternoon!" said Scrooge.

"And A Happy New Year!"

"Good afternoon!" said Scrooge.

His nephew left the room without an angry word, notwithstanding. He stopped at the outer door to bestow the greetings of the season on the clerk, who, cold as he was, was warmer than Scrooge; for he returned them cordially.

"There's another fellow," muttered Scrooge; who overheard him: "my clerk, with fifteen shillings a-week, and a wife and family, talking about a merry Christmas. I'll retire to Bedlam."

This lunatic, in letting Scrooge's nephew out, had let two other people in. They were portly gentlemen, pleasant to behold, and now stood, with their hats off, in Scrooge's office. They had books and papers in their hands, and bowed to him.

"Scrooge and Marley's, I believe," said one of the gentlemen, referring to his list. "Have I the pleasure of addressing Mr. Scrooge, or Mr. Marley?"

"Mr. Marley has been dead these seven years," Scrooge replied. "He died seven years ago, this very night."

"We have no doubt his liberality is well represented by his surviving partner," said the gentleman, presenting his credentials.

It certainly was; for they had been two kindred spirits. At the ominous word "liberality," Scrooge frowned, and shook his head, and handed the credentials back.

"At this festive season of the year, Mr. Scrooge," said the gentleman, taking up a pen, "it is more than usually desirable that we should make some slight provision for the poor and destitute, who suffer greatly at the present time. Many thousands are in want of common necessaries; hundreds of thousands are in want of common comforts, sir."

"Are there no prisons?" asked Scrooge.

"Plenty of prisons," said the gentleman, laying down the pen again.

"And the Union workhouses?" demanded Scrooge. "Are they still in operation?"

"They are. Still," returned the gentleman, "I wish I could say they were not."

"The Treadmill and the Poor Law are in full vigour, then?" said Scrooge.

"Both very busy, sir."

"Oh! I was afraid, from what you said at first, that something had occurred to stop them in their useful course," said Scrooge. "I'm very glad to hear it."

"Under the impression that they scarcely furnish Christian cheer of mind or body to the multitude," returned the gentleman, "a few of us are endeavouring to raise a fund to buy the Poor some meat and drink, and means of warmth. We choose this time because it is a time, of all others, when Want is keenly felt, and Abundance rejoices. What shall I put you down for?"

"Nothing!" Scrooge replied.

"You wish to be anonymous?"

"I wish to be left alone," said Scrooge. "Since you ask me what I wish, gentlemen, that is my answer. I don't make merry myself at Christmas, and I can't afford to make idle people merry. I help to support the establishments I have mentioned: they cost enough: and those who are badly off must go there."

"Many can't go there; and many would rather die."

"If they would rather die," said Scrooge, "they had better do it, and decrease the surplus population. Besides–excuse me–I don't know that."

"But you might know it," observed the gentleman.

"It's not my business," Scrooge returned. "It's enough for a man to understand his own business, and not to interfere with other people's. Mine occupies me constantly. Good afternoon, gentlemen!"

Seeing clearly that it would be useless to pursue their point, the gentlemen withdrew. Scrooge resumed his labours with an improved opinion of himself, and in a more facetious temper than was usual with him.

Meanwhile the fog and darkness thickened so, that people ran about with flaring links, proffering their services to go before horses in carriages, and conduct them on their way. The ancient tower of a church, whose gruff old bell was always peeping slily down at Scrooge out of a gothic window in the wall, became invisible, and struck the hours and quarters in the clouds, with tremulous vibrations afterwards, as if its teeth were chattering in its frozen head up there. The cold became intense. In the main street, at the corner of the court, some labourers were repairing the gas-pipes, and had lighted a great fire in a brazier, round which a party of ragged men and boys were gathered: warming their hands and winking their eyes before the blaze in rapture. The water-plug being left in solitude, its overflowings sullenly congealed, and turned to misanthropic ice. The brightness of the shops where holly sprigs and berries crackled in the lamp-heat of the windows, made pale faces ruddy as they passed. Poulterers' and grocers' trades became a splendid joke: a glorious pageant, with which it was next to impossible to believe that such dull principles as bargain and sale had anything to do. The Lord Mayor, in the stronghold of the mighty Mansion House, gave orders to his fifty cooks and butlers to keep Christmas as a Lord Mayor's household should; and even the little tailor, whom he had fined five shillings on the previous Monday for being drunk and blood-thirsty in the streets, stirred up to-morrow's pudding in his garret, while his lean wife and the baby sallied out to buy the beef.

Foggier yet, and colder! Piercing, searching, biting cold. If the good Saint Dunstan had but nipped the Evil Spirit's nose with a touch of such weather as that, instead of using his familiar weapons, then indeed he would have roared to lusty purpose. The owner of one scant young nose, gnawed and mumbled by the hungry cold as bones are gnawed by dogs, stooped down at Scrooge's keyhole to regale him with a Christmas carol: but at the first sound of–*"God bless you merry gentleman! May nothing you dismay!"* Scrooge seized the ruler with such energy of action, that the singer fled in terror, leaving the keyhole to the fog and even more congenial frost.

At length the hour of shutting up the counting-house arrived. With an ill-will Scrooge dismounted from his stool, and tacitly admitted the fact to the expectant clerk in the Tank, who instantly snuffed his candle out, and put on his hat.

"You'll want all day to-morrow, I suppose?" said Scrooge.

"If quite convenient, sir."

"It's not convenient," said Scrooge, "and it's not fair. If I was to stop half-a-crown for it, you'd think yourself ill used, I'll be bound?"

The clerk smiled faintly.

"And yet," said Scrooge, "you don't think *me* ill used, when I pay a day's wages for no work."

The clerk observed that it was only once a year.

"A poor excuse for picking a man's pocket every twenty-fifth of December!" said Scrooge, buttoning his great-coat to the chin. "But I suppose you must have the whole day. Be here all the earlier next morning!"

The clerk promised that he would; and Scrooge walked out with a growl. The office was closed in a twinkling, and the clerk, with the long ends of his white comforter dangling below his waist (for he boasted no great-coat), went down a slide on Cornhill, at the end of a lane of boys, twenty times, in honour of its being Christmas-eve, and then ran home to Camden Town as hard as he could pelt, to play at blindman's-buff.

Scrooge took his melancholy dinner in his usual melancholy tavern; and having read all the newspapers, and beguiled the rest of the evening with his banker's-book, went home to bed. He lived in chambers which had once belonged to his deceased partner. They were a gloomy suite of rooms, in a lowering pile of building up a yard, where it had so little business to be, that one could scarcely help fancying it must have run there when it was a young house, playing at hide-and-seek with other houses, and have forgotten the way out again. It was old enough now, and dreary enough, for nobody lived in it but Scrooge, the other rooms being all let out as offices. The yard was so dark that even Scrooge, who knew its every stone, was fain to grope with his hands. The fog and frost so hung about the black old gateway of the house, that it seemed as if the Genius of the Weather sat in mournful meditation on the threshold.

Now, it is a fact, that there was nothing at all particular about the knocker on the door, except that it was very large. It is also a fact, that Scrooge had seen it night and morning during his whole residence in that place; also that Scrooge had as little of what is called fancy about him as any man in the City of London, even including–which is a bold word–the corporation, aldermen, and livery. Let it also be borne in mind that Scrooge had not bestowed one thought on Marley, since his last mention of his seven-years' dead partner that afternoon. And then let any man explain to me, if he can, how it happened that Scrooge, having his key in the lock of the door, saw in the knocker, without its undergoing any intermediate process of change: not a knocker, but Marley's face.

Marley's face. It was not in impenetrable shadow as the other objects in the yard were, but had a dismal light about it, like a bad lobster in a dark cellar. It was not angry or ferocious, but looked at Scrooge as Marley used to look: with ghostly spectacles turned up upon its ghostly forehead. The hair was curiously stirred, as if by breath or hot-air; and though the eyes were wide open, they were perfectly motionless. That, and its livid colour, made it horrible; but its horror seemed to be, in spite of the face and beyond its control, rather than a part of its own expression.

As Scrooge looked fixedly at this phenomenon, it was a knocker again.

To say that he was not startled, or that his blood was not conscious of a terrible sensation to which it had been a stranger from infancy, would be untrue. But he put his hand upon the key he had relinquished, turned it sturdily, walked in, and lighted his candle.

He *did* pause, with a moment's irresolution, before he shut the door; and he *did* look cautiously behind it first, as if he half-expected to be terrified with the sight of Marley's pigtail sticking out into the hall. But there was nothing on the back of the door, except the screws and nuts that held the knocker on; so he said "Pooh, pooh!" and closed it with a bang.

The sound resounded through the house like thunder. Every room above, and every cask in the wine-merchant's cellars below, appeared to have a separate peal of echoes of its own. Scrooge was not a man to be frightened by echoes. He fastened the door, and walked across the hall, and up the stairs: slowly too: trimming his candle as he went.

You may talk vaguely about driving a coach-and-six up a good old flight of stairs, or through a bad young Act of Parliament; but I mean to say you might have got a hearse up that staircase, and taken it broadwise, with the splinter-bar towards the wall, and the door towards the balustrades: and done it easy. There was plenty of width for that, and room to spare; which is perhaps the reason why Scrooge thought he saw a locomotive hearse going on before him in the gloom. Half a dozen gas-lamps out of the street wouldn't have lighted the entry too well, so you may suppose that it was pretty dark with Scrooge's dip.

Up Scrooge went, not caring a button for that: darkness is cheap, and Scrooge liked it. But before he shut his heavy door, he walked through his rooms to see that all was right. He had just enough recollection of the face to desire to do that.

Sitting room, bed-room, lumber-room. All as they should be. Nobody under the table, nobody under the sofa; a small fire in the grate; spoon and basin ready; and the little saucepan of gruel (Scrooge had a cold in his head) upon the hob. Nobody under the bed; nobody in the closet; nobody in his dressing-gown, which was hanging up in a suspicious attitude against the wall. Lumber-room as usual. Old fire-guard, old shoes, two fish-baskets, washing-stand on three legs, and a poker.

Quite satisfied, he closed his door, and locked himself in; double-locked himself in, which was not his custom. Thus secured against surprise, he took off his cravat; put on his dressing-gown and slippers, and his night-cap; and sat down before the fire to take his gruel.

It was a very low fire indeed; nothing on such a bitter night. He was obliged to sit close to it, and brood over it, before he could extract the least sensation of warmth from such a handful of fuel. The fireplace was an old one, built by some Dutch merchant long ago, and paved all round with quaint Dutch tiles, designed to illustrate the Scriptures. There were Cains and Abels; Pharaoh's daughters, Queens of Sheba, Angelic messengers descending through the air on clouds like feather-beds, Abrahams, Belshazzars, Apostles putting off to sea in butter-boats, hundreds of figures to attract his thoughts; and yet that face of Marley, seven years dead, came like the ancient Prophet's rod, and swallowed up the whole. If each smooth tile had been a blank at first, with power to shape some picture on its surface from the disjointed fragments of his thoughts, there would have been a copy of old Marley's head on every one.

"Humbug!" said Scrooge; and walked across the room.

After several turns, he sat down again. As he threw his head back in the chair, his glance happened to rest upon a bell, a disused bell, that hung in the room, and communicated for some purpose now forgotten with a chamber in the highest story of the building. It was with great astonishment, and with a strange, inexplicable dread, that as he looked, he saw this bell begin to swing. It swung so softly in the outset that it scarcely made a sound; but soon it rang out loudly, and so did every bell in the house.

This might have lasted half a minute, or a minute, but it seemed an hour. The bells ceased as they had begun, together. They were succeeded by a clanking noise, deep down below; as if some person were dragging a heavy chain over the casks in the wine-merchant's cellar. Scrooge then remembered to have heard that ghosts in haunted houses were described as dragging chains.

The cellar-door flew open with a booming sound, and then he heard the noise much louder, on the floors below; then coming up the stairs; then coming straight towards his door.

"It's humbug still!" said Scrooge. "I won't believe it."

His colour changed though, when, without a pause, it came on through the heavy door, and passed into the room before his eyes. Upon its coming in, the dying flame leaped up, as though it cried "I know him! Marley's Ghost!" and fell again.

The same face: the very same. Marley in his pig-tail, usual waistcoat, tights, and boots; the tassels on the latter bristling, like his pigtail, and his coat-skirts, and the hair upon his head. The chain he drew was clasped about his middle. It was long, and wound about him like a tail; and it was made (for Scrooge observed it closely) of cash-boxes, keys, padlocks, ledgers, deeds, and heavy purses wrought in steel. His body was transparent: so that Scrooge, observing him, and looking through his waistcoat, could see the two buttons on his coat behind.

Scrooge had often heard it said that Marley had no bowels, but he had never believed it until now.

No, nor did he believe it even now. Though he looked the phantom through and through, and saw it standing before him; though he felt the chilling influence of its death-cold eyes; and marked the very texture of the folded kerchief bound about its head and chin, which wrapper he had not observed before: he was still incredulous,

"Marley's Ghost," original color illustration by John Leech (1843). Courtesy Beinecke Rare Book and Manuscript Library, Yale University.

and fought against his senses.

"How now!" said Scrooge, caustic and cold as ever. "What do you want with me?"

"Much!"–Marley's voice, no doubt about it.

"Who are you?"

"Ask me who I *was*."

"Who *were* you then?" said Scrooge, raising his voice. "You're particular–for a shade." He was going to say *"to* a shade," but substituted this, as more appropriate.

"In life I was your partner, Jacob Marley."

"Can you–can you sit down?" asked Scrooge, looking doubtfully at him.

"I can."

"Do it then."

Scrooge asked the question, because he didn't know whether a ghost so transparent might find himself in a condition to take a chair; and felt that in the event of its being impossible, it might involve the necessity of an embarrassing explanation. But the ghost sat down on the opposite side of the fireplace, as if he were quite used to it.

"You don't believe in me," observed the Ghost.

"I don't," said Scrooge.

"What evidence would you have of my reality, beyond that of your senses?"

"I don't know," said Scrooge.

"Why do you doubt your senses?"

"Because," said Scrooge, "a little thing affects them. A slight disorder of the stomach makes them cheats. You may be an undigested bit of beef, a blot of mustard, a crumb of cheese, a fragment of an underdone potato. There's more of gravy than of grave about you, whatever you are!"

Scrooge was not much in the habit of cracking

jokes, nor did he feel, in his heart, by any means waggish then. The truth is, that he tried to be smart, as a means of distracting his own attention, and keeping down his terror; for the spectre's voice disturbed the very marrow in his bones.

To sit, staring at those fixed, glazed eyes, in silence for a moment, would play, Scrooge felt, the very deuce with him. There was something very awful, too, in the spectre's being provided with an infernal atmosphere of its own. Scrooge could not feel it himself, but this was clearly the case; for though the Ghost sat perfectly motionless, its hair, and skirts, and tassels, were still agitated as by the hot vapour from an oven.

"You see this toothpick?" said Scrooge, returning quickly to the charge, for the reason just assigned; and wishing, though it were only for a second, to divert the vision's stony gaze from himself.

"I do," replied the Ghost.

"You are not looking at it," said Scrooge.

"But I see it," said the Ghost, "notwithstanding."

"Well!" returned Scrooge. "I have but to swallow this, and be for the rest of my days persecuted by a legion of goblins, all of my own creation. Humbug, I tell you–humbug!"

At this, the spirit raised a frightful cry, and shook its chain with such a dismal and appalling noise, that Scrooge held on tight to his chair, to save himself from falling in a swoon. But how much greater was his horror, when the phantom taking off the bandage round its head, as if it were too warm to wear in-doors, its lower jaw dropped down upon its breast!

Scrooge fell upon his knees, and clasped his hands before his face.

"Mercy!" he said. "Dreadful apparition, why do you trouble me?"

"Man of the worldly mind!" replied the Ghost, "do you believe in me or not?"

"I do," said Scrooge. "I must. But why do spirits walk the earth, and why do they come to me?"

"It is required of every man," the Ghost returned, "that the spirit within him should walk abroad among his fellow-men, and travel far and wide; and if that spirit goes not forth in life, it is condemned to do so after death. It is doomed to wander through the world–oh, woe is me!–and witness what it cannot share, but might have shared on earth, and turned to happiness!"

Again the spectre raised a cry, and shook its chain and wrung its shadowy hands.

"You are fettered," said Scrooge, trembling. "Tell me why?"

"I wear the chain I forged in life," replied the Ghost. "I made it link by link, and yard by yard; I girded it on of my own free will, and of my own free will I wore it. Is its pattern strange to *you*?"

Scrooge trembled more and more.

"Or would you know," pursued the Ghost, "the weight and length of the strong coil you bear yourself? It was full as heavy and as long as this, seven Christmas Eves ago. You have laboured on it, since. It is a ponderous chain!"

Scrooge glanced about him on the floor, in the expectation of finding himself surrounded by some fifty or sixty fathoms of iron cable: but he could see nothing.

"Jacob," he said, imploringly. "Old Jacob Marley, tell me more. Speak comfort to me, Jacob."

"I have none to give," the Ghost replied. "It comes from other regions, Ebenezer Scrooge, and is conveyed by other ministers, to other kinds of men. Nor can I tell you what I would. A very little more is all permitted to me. I cannot rest, I cannot stay, I cannot linger anywhere. My spirit never walked beyond our counting-house–mark me!–in life my spirit never roved beyond the narrow limits of our money-changing hole; and weary journeys lie before me!"

It was a habit with Scrooge, whenever he became thoughtful, to put his hands in his breeches pockets. Pondering on what the Ghost had said, he did so now, but without lifting up his eyes, or getting off his knees.

"You must have been very slow about it, Jacob," Scrooge observed, in a business-like manner, though with humility and deference.

"Slow!" the Ghost repeated.

"Seven years dead," mused Scrooge. "And travelling all the time?"

"The whole time," said the Ghost. "No rest, no peace. Incessant torture of remorse."

"You travel fast?" said Scrooge.

"On the wings of the wind," replied the Ghost.

"You might have got over a great quantity of ground in seven years," said Scrooge.

The Ghost, on hearing this, set up another cry, and clanked its chain so hideously in the dead silence of the night, that the Ward would have been justified in indicting it for a nuisance.

"Oh! captive, bound, and double-ironed," cried the phantom, "not to know, that ages of incessant labour by immortal creatures, for this earth must pass into eternity before the good of which it is susceptible is all developed. Not to know that any Christian spirit working kindly in its little sphere, whatever it may be, will find its mortal life too short for its vast means of usefulness. Not to know that no space of regret can make amends for one life's opportunity misused! Yet such was I! Oh! such was I!"

"But you were always a good man of business, Jacob," faultered Scrooge, who now began to apply this to himself.

"Business!" cried the Ghost, wringing its hands again. "Mankind was my business. The common welfare was my business; charity, mercy, forbearance, and benevolence, were, all, my business. The dealings of my trade were but a drop of water in the comprehensive ocean of my business!"

It held up its chain at arm's length, as if that were the cause of all its unavailing grief, and flung it heavily upon the ground again.

"At this time of the rolling year," the spectre said, "I suffer most. Why did I walk through crowds of fellow-beings with my eyes turned down, and never raise them to that blessed Star which led the Wise Men to a poor abode? Were there no poor homes to which its light would have conducted *me!*"

Scrooge was very much dismayed to hear the spectre going on at this rate, and began to quake exceedingly.

"Hear me!" cried the Ghost. "My time is nearly gone."

"I will," said Scrooge. "But don't be hard upon me! Don't be flowery, Jacob! Pray!"

"How it is that I appear before you in a shape that you can see, I may not tell. I have sat invisible beside you many and many a day."

It was not an agreeable idea. Scrooge shivered, and wiped the perspiration from his brow.

"That is no light part of my penance," pursued the Ghost. "I am here to-night to warn you, that you have yet a chance and hope of escaping my fate. A chance and hope of my procuring, Ebenezer."

"You were always a good friend to me," said Scrooge. "Thank'ee!"

"You will be haunted," resumed the Ghost, "by Three Spirits."

Scrooge's countenance fell almost as low as the Ghost's had done.

"Is that the chance and hope you mentioned, Jacob?" he demanded, in a faultering voice.

"It is."

"I–I think I'd rather not," said Scrooge.

"Without their visits," said the Ghost, "you cannot hope to shun the path I tread. Expect the first to-morrow, when the bell tolls one."

"Couldn't I take 'em all at once, and have it over, Jacob?" hinted Scrooge.

"Expect the second on the next night at the same hour. The third upon the next night when the last stroke of twelve has ceased to vibrate. Look to see me no more; and look that, for your own sake, you remember what has passed between us!"

When it had said these words, the spectre took its wrapper from the table, and bound it round its head, as before. Scrooge knew this, by the smart sound its teeth made, when the jaws were brought together by the bandage. He ventured to raise his eyes again, and found his supernatural visitor confronting him in an erect attitude, with its chain wound over and about its arm.

The apparition walked backward from him; and at every step it took, the window raised itself a little, so that when the spectre reached it, it was wide open. It beckoned Scrooge to approach, which he did. When they were within two paces of each other, Marley's Ghost held up its hand, warning him to come no nearer. Scrooge stopped.

Not so much in obedience, as in surprise and fear: for on the raising of the hand, he became sensible of confused noises in the air; incoherent sounds of lamentation and regret; wailings inexpressibly sorrowful and self-accusatory. The spectre, after listening for a moment, joined in the mournful dirge; and floated out upon the bleak, dark night.

Scrooge followed to the window: desperate in his curiosity. He looked out.

The air filled with phantoms, wandering hither and thither in restless haste, and moaning as they went. Every one of them wore chains like Marley's Ghost; some few (they might be guilty governments) were linked together; none were free. Many had been personally known to Scrooge in their lives. He had been quite familiar with one old ghost, in a white waistcoat, with a monstrous iron safe attached to its ankle, who cried piteously at being unable to assist a wretched woman with an infant, whom it saw below, upon a door-step. The misery with them all was, clearly, that they sought to interfere, for good, in human matters, and had lost the power for ever.

Whether these creatures faded into mist, or mist enshrouded them, he could not tell. But they and their spirit voices faded together; and the night became as it had been when he walked home.

Scrooge closed the window, and examined the door by which the Ghost had entered. It was double-locked, as he had locked it with his own hands, and the bolts were undisturbed. He tried to say "Humbug!" but stopped at the first syllable. And being, from the emotion he had undergone, or the fatigues of the day, or his glimpse of the Invisible World, or the dull conversation of the Ghost, or the lateness of the hour, much in need of repose; went straight to bed, without undressing, and fell asleep upon the instant.

Stave

The First of the Three Spirits

When Scrooge awoke, it was so dark, that looking out of bed, he could scarcely distinguish the transparent window from the opaque walls of his chamber. He was endeavouring to pierce the darkness with his ferret eyes, when the chimes of a neighbouring church struck the four quarters. So he listened for the hour.

To his great astonishment the heavy bell went on from six to seven, and from seven to eight, and regularly up to twelve; then stopped. Twelve! It was past two when he went to bed. The clock was wrong. An icicle must have got into the works. Twelve!

He touched the spring of his repeater, to correct this most preposterous clock. Its rapid little pulse beat twelve; and stopped.

"Why, it isn't possible," said Scrooge, "that I can have slept through a whole day and far into another night. It isn't possible that anything has happened to the sun, and this is twelve at noon!"

The idea being an alarming one, he scrambled out of bed, and groped his way to the window. He was obliged to rub the frost off with the sleeve of his dressing-gown before he could see anything; and could see very little then. All he could make out was, that it was still very foggy and extremely cold, and that there was no noise of people running to and fro, and making a great stir, as there unquestionably would have been if night had beaten off bright day, and taken possession of the world. This was a great relief, because "three days after sight of this First of Exchange pay to Mr. Ebenezer Scrooge or his order," and so forth, would have become a mere United States' security if there were no days to count by.

Scrooge went to bed again, and thought, and thought, and thought it over and over and over, and could make nothing of it. The more he thought, the more perplexed he was; and the more he endeavoured not to think, the more he thought. Marley's Ghost bothered him exceedingly. Every time he resolved within himself, after mature inquiry, that it was all a dream, his mind flew back again, like a strong spring released, to its first position, and presented the same problem to be worked all through, "Was it a dream or not?"

Scrooge lay in this state until the chimes had gone three quarters more, when he remembered, on a sudden, that the Ghost had warned him of a visitation when the bell tolled one. He resolved to lie awake until the hour was passed; and, considering that he could no more go to sleep than go to Heaven, this was perhaps the wisest resolution in his power.

The quarter was so long, that he was more than once convinced he must have sunk into a doze unconsciously, and missed the clock. At length it broke upon his listening ear.

"Ding, dong!"

"A quarter past," said Scrooge, counting.

"Ding, dong!"

"Half past!" said Scrooge.

"Ding, dong!"

"A quarter to it," said Scrooge.

"Ding, dong!"

"The hour itself," said Scrooge, triumphantly, "and nothing else!"

He spoke before the hour bell sounded, which it now did with a deep, dull, hollow, melancholy ONE. Light flashed up in the room upon the instant, and the curtains of his bed were drawn.

The curtains of his bed were drawn aside, I tell you, by a hand. Not the curtains at his feet, nor the curtains at his back, but those to which his face was addressed. The curtains of his bed were drawn aside; and Scrooge, starting up into a half-recumbent attitude, found himself face to face with the unearthly visitor who drew them: as close to it as I am now to you, and I am standing in the spirit at your elbow.

It was a strange figure–like a child: yet not so like a child as like an old man, viewed through some supernatural medium, which gave him the appearance of having receded from the view, and being diminished to a child's proportions. Its hair, which hung about its neck and down its back, was white as if with age; and yet the face had not a wrinkle in it, and the tenderest bloom was on the skin. The arms were very long and muscular; the hands the same, as if its hold were of uncommon strength. Its legs and feet, most delicately formed, were, like those upper members, bare. It wore a tunic of the purest white; and round its waist was bound a lustrous belt, the sheen of which was beautiful. It held a branch of fresh green holly in its hand; and, in singular contradiction of that wintry emblem, had its dress trimmed with summer flowers. But the strangest thing about it was, that from the crown of its head there sprung a bright clear jet of light, by which all this was visible; and which was doubtless the occasion of its using, in its duller moments, a great extinguisher for a cap, which it now held under its arm.

Even this, though, when Scrooge looked at it with increasing steadiness, was *not* its strangest quality. For as its belt sparkled and glittered now in one part and now in another, and what was light one instant, at another time was dark, so the figure itself fluctuated in its distinctness: being now a thing with one arm, now with one leg, now with twenty legs, now a pair of legs without a head, now a head without a body: of which dissolving parts, no outline would be visible in the dense gloom wherein they melted away. And in the very wonder of this, it would be itself again; distinct and clear as ever.

"Are you the Spirit, sir, whose coming was foretold to me?" asked Scrooge.

"I am!"

The voice was soft and gentle. Singularly low, as if instead of being so close beside him, it were at a distance.

"Who, and what are you?" Scrooge demanded.

"I am the Ghost of Christmas Past."

"Long Past?" inquired Scrooge: observant of its dwarfish stature.

"No. Your past."

Perhaps, Scrooge could not have told anybody why, if anybody could have asked him; but he had a special desire to see the Spirit in his cap; and begged him to be covered.

"What!" exclaimed the Ghost, "would you so soon put out, with worldly hands, the light I give? Is it not enough that you are one of those whose passions made this cap, and force me through whole trains of years to wear it low upon my brow!"

Scrooge reverently disclaimed all intention to offend, or any knowledge of having wilfully "bonneted" the Spirit at any period of his life. He then made bold to inquire what business brought him there.

"Your welfare!" said the Ghost.

Scrooge expressed himself much obliged, but could not help thinking that a night of unbroken rest would have been more conducive to that end. The Spirit must have heard him thinking for it said immediately:

"Your reclamation, then. Take heed!"

It put out its strong hand as it spoke, and clasped him gently by the arm.

"Rise! and walk with me!"

It would have been in vain for Scrooge to plead that the weather and the hour were not adapted to pedestrian purposes; that bed was warm, and the thermometer a long way below freezing; that he was clad but lightly in his slippers, dressing-gown, and nightcap; and that he had a cold upon him at that time. The grasp, though gentle as a woman's hand, was not to be resisted. He rose: but finding that the Spirit made towards the window, clasped its robe in supplication.

"I am a mortal," Scrooge remonstrated, "and liable to fall."

"Bear but a touch of my hand *there*," said the Spirit, laying it upon his heart, "and you shall be upheld in more than this!"

As the words were spoken, they passed through the wall, and stood upon an open country road, with fields on either hand. The city had entirely vanished. Not a vestige of it was to be seen. The darkness and the mist had vanished with it, for it was a clear, cold, winter day, with snow upon the ground.

"Good Heaven!" said Scrooge, clasping his hands together, as he looked about him. "I was bred in this place. I was a boy here!"

The Spirit gazed upon him mildly. Its gentle touch, though it had been light and instantaneous, appeared still present to the old man's sense of feeling. He was conscious of a thousand odours floating in the air, each one connected with a thousand thoughts, and hopes, and joys, and cares long, long, forgotten!

"Your lip is trembling," said the Ghost. "And what is that upon your cheek?"

Scrooge muttered, with an unusual catching in his voice, that it was a pimple; and begged the Ghost to lead him where he would.

"You recollect the way?" inquired the Spirit.

"Remember it!" cried Scrooge with fervour–"I could walk it blindfold."

"Strange to have forgotten it for so many years!" observed the Ghost. "Let us go on."

They walked along the road; Scrooge recognising every gate, and post, and tree; until a little market-town appeared in the distance, with its bridge, its church, and winding river. Some shaggy ponies now were seen trotting towards them with boys upon their backs, who called to other boys in country gigs and carts, driven by farmers. All these boys were in great spirits, and shouted to each other, until the broad fields were so full of merry music, that the crisp air laughed to hear it.

"These are but shadows of the things that have been," said the Ghost. "They have no consciousness of us."

The jocund travellers came on; and as they came, Scrooge knew and named them every one. Why was he rejoiced beyond all bounds to see them! Why did his cold eye glisten, and his heart leap up as they went past! Why was he filled with gladness when he heard them give each other Merry Christmas, as they parted at cross-roads and bye-ways, for their several homes! What was merry Christmas to Scrooge? Out upon merry Christmas! What good had it ever done to him?

"The school is not quite deserted," said the Ghost. "A solitary child, neglected by his friends, is left there still."

Scrooge said he knew it. And he sobbed.

They left the high-road, by a well remembered lane, and soon approached a mansion of dull red brick, with a little weathercock-surmounted cupola on the roof, and a bell hanging in it. It was a large house, but one of broken fortunes; for the spacious offices were little used, their walls were damp and mossy, their windows broken, and their gates decayed. Fowls clucked and strutted in the stables; and the coach-houses and sheds were over-run with grass. Nor was it more retentive of its ancient state, within; for entering the dreary hall, and glancing through the open doors of many rooms, they found them poorly furnished, cold, and vast. There was an earthy savour in the air, a chilly bareness in the place, which associated itself somehow with too much getting up by candle-light, and not too much to eat.

They went, the Ghost and Scrooge, across the hall, to a door at the back of the house. It opened before them, and disclosed a long, bare, melancholy room, made barer still by lines of plain deal forms and desks. At one of these a lonely boy was reading near a feeble fire; and Scrooge sat down upon a form, and wept to see his poor forgotten self as he had used to be.

Not a latent echo in the house, not a squeak and scuffle from the mice behind the panelling, not a drip from the half-thawed water-spout in the dull yard behind, not a sigh among the leafless boughs of one despondent poplar, not the idle swinging of an empty store-house door, no, not a clicking in the fire, but fell upon the heart of Scrooge with a softening influence, and gave a freer passage to his tears.

The Spirit touched him on the arm, and pointed to his younger self, intent upon his reading. Suddenly a man, in foreign garments: wonderfully real and distinct to look at: stood outside the window, with an axe stuck in his belt, and leading an ass laden with wood by the bridle.

"Why, it's Ali Baba!" Scrooge exclaimed in ecstasy. "It's dear old honest Ali Baba! Yes, yes, I know! One Christmas time, when yonder solitary child was left here all alone, he *did* come, for the first time, just like that. Poor boy! And Valentine," said Scrooge, "and his wild brother, Orson; there they go! And what's his name, who was put down in his drawers, asleep, at the Gate of Damascus; don't you see him! And the Sultan's Groom turned upside-down by the Genii; there he is upon his head! Serve him right. I'm glad of it. What business had *he* to be married to the Princess!"

To hear Scrooge expending all the earnestness of his nature on such subjects, in a most extraordinary voice between laughing and crying; and to see his heightened and excited face; would have been a surprise to his business friends in the city, indeed.

"There's the Parrot!" cried Scrooge. "Green body and yellow tail, with a thing like a lettuce growing out of the top of his head; there he is! Poor Robin Crusoe, he called him, when he came home again after sailing round the island. 'Poor Robin Crusoe, where have you been, Robin Crusoe?' The man thought he was dreaming, but he wasn't. It was the Parrot, you know. There goes Friday, running for his life to the little creek! Halloa! Hoop! Halloo!"

Then, with a rapidity of transition very foreign to his usual character, he said, in pity for his former self, "Poor boy!" and cried again.

"I wish," Scrooge muttered, putting his hand in his pocket, and looking about him, after drying his eyes with his cuff: "but it's too late now."

"What is the matter?" asked the Spirit.

"Nothing," said Scrooge. "Nothing. There was a boy singing a Christmas Carol at my door last night. I should like to have given him something: that's all."

The Ghost smiled thoughtfully, and waved its hand: saying as it did so, "Let us see another Christmas!"

Scrooge's former self grew larger at the words, and the room became a little darker and more dirty. The panels shrunk, the windows cracked; fragments of plaster fell out of the ceiling, and the naked laths were shown instead; but how all this was brought about, Scrooge knew no more than you do. He only knew that it was quite correct; that everything had happened so; that there he was, alone again, when all the other boys had gone home for the jolly holidays.

He was not reading now, but walking up and down despairingly. Scrooge looked at the Ghost, and with a mournful shaking of his head, glanced anxiously towards the door.

It opened; and a little girl, much younger than the boy, came darting in, and putting her arms about his neck, and often kissing him, addressed him as her "Dear, dear brother."

"I have come to bring you home, dear brother!" said the child, clapping her tiny hands, and bending down to laugh. "To bring you home, home, home!"

"Home, little Fan?" returned the boy.

"Yes!" said the child, brimful of glee. "Home, for good and all. Home, for ever and ever. Father is so much kinder than he used to be, that home's like

Heaven! He spoke so gently to me one dear night when I was going to bed, that I was not afraid to ask him once more if you might come home; and he said Yes, you should; and sent me in a coach to bring you. And you're to be a man!" said the child, opening her eyes, "and are never to come back here; but first, we're to be together all the Christmas long, and have the merriest time in all the world."

"You are quite a woman, little Fan!" exclaimed the boy.

She clapped her hands and laughed, and tried to touch his head; but being too little, laughed again, and stood on tiptoe to embrace him. Then she began to drag him, in her childish eagerness, towards the door; and he, nothing loth to go, accompanied her.

A terrible voice in the hall cried, "Bring down Master Scrooge's box, there!" and in the hall appeared the schoolmaster himself, who glared on Master Scrooge with a ferocious condescension, and threw him into a dreadful state of mind by shaking hands with him. He then conveyed him and his sister into the veriest old well of a shivering best-parlour that ever was seen, where the maps upon the wall, and the celestial and terrestrial globes in the windows were waxy with cold. Here he produced a decanter of curiously light wine, and a block of curiously heavy cake, and administered instalments of those dainties to the young people: at the same time, sending out a meagre servant to offer a glass of "something" to the postboy, who answered that he thanked the gentleman, but if it was the same tap as he had tasted before, he had rather not. Master Scrooge's trunk being by this time tied on to the top of the chaise, the children bade the schoolmaster good-bye right willingly; and getting into it, drove gaily down the garden-sweep: the quick wheels dashing the hoar-frost and snow from off the dark leaves of the evergreens like spray.

"Always a delicate creature, whom a breath might have withered," said the Ghost. "But she had a large heart!"

"So she had," cried Scrooge. "You're right. I'll not gainsay it, Spirit. God forbid!"

"She died a woman," said the Ghost, "and had, as I think, children."

"One child," Scrooge returned.

"True," said the Ghost. "Your nephew!"

Scrooge seemed uneasy in his mind; and answered briefly, "Yes."

Although they had but that moment left the school behind them, they were now in the busy thoroughfares of a city, where shadowy passengers passed and repassed; where shadowy carts and coaches battled for the way, and all the strife and tumult of a real city were. It was made plain enough, by the dressing of the shops, that here too it was Christmas time again; but it was evening, and the streets were lighted up.

The Ghost stopped at a certain warehouse door, and asked Scrooge if he knew it.

"Know it!" said Scrooge. "Was I apprenticed here?"

They went in. At sight of an old gentleman in a Welch wig, sitting behind such a high desk, that if he had been two inches taller he must have knocked his head against the ceiling, Scrooge cried in great excitement:

"Why, it's old Fezziwig! Bless his heart; it's Fezziwig alive again!"

Old Fezziwig laid down his pen, and looked up

at the clock, which pointed to the hour of seven. He rubbed his hands; adjusted his capacious waistcoat; laughed all over himself, from his shoes to his organ of benevolence; and called out in a comfortable, oily, rich, fat, jovial voice:

"Yo ho, there! Ebenezer! Dick!"

Scrooge's former self, now grown a young man, came briskly in, accompanied by his fellow-'prentice.

"Dick Wilkins, to be sure!" said Scrooge to the Ghost. "Bless me, yes. There he is. He was very much attached to me, was Dick. Poor Dick! Dear, dear!"

"Yo ho, my boys!" said Fezziwig. "No more work tonight. Christmas Eve, Dick. Christmas, Ebenezer! Let's have the shutters up," cried old Fezziwig, with a sharp clap of his hands, "before a man can say, Jack Robinson!"

You wouldn't believe how those two fellows went at it! They charged into the street with the shutters–one, two, three–had 'em up in their places–four, five, six–barred 'em and pinned 'em–seven, eight, nine–and came back before you could have got to twelve, panting like race-horses.

"Hilli-ho!" cried old Fezziwig, skipping down from the high desk, with wonderful agility. "Clear away, my lads, and let's have lots of room here! Hilli-ho, Dick! Chirrup, Ebenezer!"

Clear away! There was nothing they wouldn't have cleared away, or couldn't have cleared away, with old Fezziwig looking on. It was done in a minute. Every movable was packed off, as if it were dismissed from public life for evermore; the floor was swept and watered, the lamps were trimmed, fuel was heaped upon the fire; and the warehouse was as snug, and warm, and dry, and bright a ball-room, as you would desire to see upon a winter's night.

In came a fiddler with a music-book, and went up to the lofty desk, and made an orchestra of it, and tuned like fifty stomach-aches. In came Mrs. Fezziwig, one vast substantial smile. In came the three Miss Fezziwigs, beaming and lovable. In came the six young followers whose hearts they broke. In came all the young men and women employed in the business. In came the housemaid, with her cousin, the baker. In came the cook, with her brother's particular friend, the milkman. In came the boy from over the way, who was suspected of not having board enough from his master; trying to hide himself behind the girl from next door but one, who was proved to have had her ears pulled by her Mistress. In they all came, one after another; some shyly, some boldly, some gracefully, some awkwardly, some pushing, some pulling; in they all came, anyhow and everyhow. Away they all went, twenty couple at once, hands half round and back again the other way; down the middle and up again; round and round in various stages of affectionate grouping; old top couple always turning up in the wrong place; new top couple starting off again, as soon as they got there; all top couples at last, and not a bottom one to help them. When this result was brought about, old Fezziwig, clapping his hands to stop the dance, cried out, "Well done!" and the fiddler plunged his hot face into a pot of porter, especially provided for that purpose. But scorning rest upon his reappearance, he instantly began again, though there were no dancers yet, as if the other fiddler had been carried home, exhausted, on a shutter; and he were a bran-new man resolved to beat him out of sight, or perish.

There were more dances, and there were forfeits, and more dances, and there was cake, and there was negus, and there was a great piece of Cold Roast, and there was a great piece of Cold Boiled, and there were mince-pies, and plenty of beer. But the great effect of the evening came after the Roast and Boiled, when the fiddler (an artful dog, mind! The sort of man who knew his business better than you or I could have told it him!) struck up "Sir Roger de Coverley." Then old Fezziwig stood out to dance with Mrs. Fezziwig. Top couple, too; with a good stiff piece of work cut out for them; three or four and twenty pair of partners; people who were not to be trifled with; people who *would* dance, and had no notion of walking.

But if they had been twice as many: ah, four times: old Fezziwig would have been a match for them, and so would Mrs. Fezziwig. As to *her,* she was worthy to be his partner in every sense of the term. If that's not high praise, tell me higher, and I'll use it. A positive light appeared to issue from Fezziwig's calves. They shone in every part of the dance like moons. You couldn't have predicted, at any given time, what would become of 'em next. And when old Fezziwig and Mrs. Fezziwig had gone all through the dance; advance and retire, hold hands with your partner; bow and curtsey; corkscrew; thread-the-needle, and back again to your place; Fezziwig "cut"–cut so deftly, that he appeared to wink with his legs, and came upon his feet again without a stagger.

When the clock struck eleven, this domestic ball broke up. Mr. and Mrs. Fezziwig took their stations, one on either side the door, and shaking hands with every person individually as he or she went out, wished him or her a Merry Christmas. When everybody had retired but the two 'prentices, they did the

"Fezziwig's Party," original color illustration by John Leech (1843). Courtesy Beinecke Rare Book and Manuscript Library, Yale University.

same to them; and thus the cheerful voices died away, and the lads were left to their beds; which were under a counter in the back-shop.

During the whole of this time, Scrooge had acted like a man out of his wits. His heart and soul were in the scene, and with his former self. He corroborated everything, remembered everything, enjoyed everything, and underwent the strangest agitation. It was not until now, when the bright faces of his former self and Dick were turned from them, that he remembered the Ghost, and became conscious that it was looking full upon him, while the light upon its head burnt very clear.

"A small matter," said the Ghost, "to make these silly folks so full of gratitude."

"Small!" echoed Scrooge.

The Spirit signed to him to listen to the two apprentices, who were pouring out their hearts in praise of Fezziwig: and when he had done so, said,

"Why! Is it not? He has spent but a few pounds of your mortal money: three or four, perhaps. Is that so much that he deserves this praise?"

"It isn't that," said Scrooge, heated by the remark, and speaking unconsciously like his former, not his latter, self. "It isn't that, Spirit. He has the power to render us happy or unhappy; to make our service light or burdensome; a pleasure or a toil. Say that his power lies in words and looks; in things so slight and insignificant that it is impossible to add and count 'em up: what then? The happiness he gives, is quite as great as if it cost a fortune."

He felt the Spirit's glance, and stopped.

"What is the matter?" asked the Ghost.

"Nothing particular," said Scrooge.

"Something, I think?" the Ghost insisted.

"No," said Scrooge, "No. I should like to be able to say a word or two to my clerk just now! That's all."

His former self turned down the lamps as he gave utterance to the wish; and Scrooge and the Ghost again stood side by side in the open air.

"My time grows short," observed the Spirit. "Quick!"

This was not addressed to Scrooge, or to any one whom he could see, but it produced an immediate effect. For again Scrooge saw himself. He was older now; a man in the prime of life. His face had not the harsh and rigid lines of later years; but it had begun to wear the signs of care and avarice. There was an eager, greedy, restless motion in the eye, which showed the passion that had taken root, and where the shadow of the growing tree would fall.

He was not alone, but sat by the side of a fair young girl in a mourning-dress: in whose eyes there were tears, which sparkled in the light that shone out of the Ghost of Christmas Past.

"It matters little," she said, softly. "To you, very little. Another idol has displaced me; and if it can cheer and comfort you in time to come, as I would have tried to do, I have no just cause to grieve."

"What Idol has displaced you?" he rejoined.

"A golden one."

"This is the even-handed dealing of the world!" he said. "There is nothing on which it is so hard as poverty; and there is nothing it professes to condemn with such severity as the pursuit of wealth!"

"You fear the world too much," she answered, gently. "All your other hopes have merged into the hope of being beyond the chance of its sordid reproach. I have seen your nobler aspirations fall off one by one, until the master-passion, Gain, engrosses you. Have I not?"

"What then?" he retorted. "Even if I have grown so much wiser, what then? I am not changed towards you."

She shook her head.

"Am I?"

"Our contract is an old one. It was made when we were both poor and content to be so, until, in good season, we could improve our worldly fortune by our patient industry. You *are* changed. When it was made, you were another man."

"I was a boy," he said impatiently.

"Your own feeling tells you that you were not what you are," she returned. "I am. That which promised happiness when we were one in heart, is fraught with misery now that we are two. How often and how keenly I have thought of this, I will not say. It is enough that I *have* thought of it, and can release you."

"Have I ever sought release?"

"In words. No. Never."

"In what, then?"

"In a changed nature; in an altered spirit; in another atmosphere of life; another Hope as its great end. In everything that made my love of any worth or value in your sight. If this had never been between us," said the girl, looking mildly, but with steadiness, upon him; "tell me, would you seek me out and try to win me now? Ah, no!"

He seemed to yield to the justice of this supposition, in spite of himself. But he said, with a struggle, "You think not."

"I would gladly think otherwise if I could," she answered, "Heaven knows! When *I* have learned a Truth like this, I know how strong and irresistible it must be. But if you were free to-day, to-morrow, yesterday, can even I believe that you would choose a dowerless girl–you who, in your very confidence with her, weigh everything by Gain: or, choosing her, if for a moment you were false enough to your one guiding principle to do so, do I not know that your repentance and regret would surely follow? I do; and I release you. With a full heart, for the love of him you once were."

He was about to speak; but with her head turned from him, she resumed.

"You may–the memory of what is past half makes me hope you will–have pain in this. A very, very brief time, and you will dismiss the recollection of it, gladly, as an unprofitable dream, from which it happened well that you awoke. May you be happy in the life you have chosen!"

She left him; and they parted.

"Spirit!" said Scrooge, "show me no more! Conduct me home. Why do you delight to torture me?"

"One shadow more!" exclaimed the Ghost.

"No more!" cried Scrooge. "No more. I don't wish to see it. Show me no more!"

But the relentless Ghost pinioned him in both his arms, and forced him to observe what happened next.

They were in another scene and place: a room, not very large or handsome, but full of comfort. Near to the winter fire sat a beautiful young girl, so like the last that Scrooge believed it was the same, until he saw *her,* now a comely matron, sitting opposite her daughter. The noise in this room was perfectly tumultuous, for there were more children there, than Scrooge in his agitated state of mind could count; and, unlike the celebrated herd in the poem, they were not forty children conducting themselves like one, but every child was conducting itself like forty. The consequences were uproarious beyond belief; but no one seemed to care; on the contrary, the mother and daughter laughed heartily, and enjoyed it very much; and the latter, soon beginning to mingle in the sports, got pillaged by the young brigands most ruthlessly. What would I not have given to be one of them! Though I never could have been so rude, no, no! I wouldn't for the wealth of all the world have crushed that braided hair, and torn it down; and for the precious little shoe, I wouldn't have plucked it off, God bless my soul! to save my life. As to measuring her waist in sport, as they did, bold young brood, I couldn't have done it; I should have expected my arm to have grown round it for a punishment, and never come straight again. And yet I should have dearly liked, I own, to have touched her lips; to have questioned her, that she might have opened them; to have looked upon the lashes of her downcast eyes, and never raised a blush; to have let loose waves of hair, an inch of which would be a keepsake beyond price: in short, I should have liked, I do confess, to have had the lightest licence of a child, and yet been man enough to know its value.

But now a knocking at the door was heard, and such a rush immediately ensued that she with laughing face and plundered dress was borne towards it the centre of a flushed and boisterous group, just in time to greet the father, who came home attended by a man laden with Christmas toys and presents. Then the shouting and the struggling, and the onslaught that was made on the defenceless porter! The scaling him with chairs for ladders, to dive into his pockets, despoil him of brown-paper parcels, hold on tight by his cravat, hug him round the neck, pommel his back, and kick his legs in irrepressible affection! The shouts of wonder and delight with which the development of every package was received! The terrible announcement that the baby had been taken in the act of putting a doll's frying-pan into his mouth, and was more than suspected of having swallowed a fictitious turkey, glued on a wooden platter! The immense relief of finding this a false alarm! The joy, and gratitude, and ecstasy! They are all indescribable alike. It is enough that by degrees the children and their emotions got out of the parlour and by one stair at a time, up to the top of the house; where they went to bed, and so subsided.

And now Scrooge looked on more attentively than ever, when the master of the house, having his daughter leaning fondly on him, sat down with her and her mother at his own fireside; and when he thought that such another creature, quite as graceful and as full of promise, might have called him father, and been a spring-time in the haggard winter of his life, his sight grew very dim indeed.

"Belle," said the husband, turning to his wife with a smile, "I saw an old friend of yours this afternoon."

"Who was it?"

"Guess!"

"How can I? Tut, don't I know," she added in the same breath, laughing as he laughed. "Mr. Scrooge."

"Mr. Scrooge it was. I passed his office window; and as it was not shut up, and he had a candle inside, I could scarcely help seeing him. His partner lies upon the point of death, I hear; and there he sat alone. Quite alone in the world, I do believe."

"Spirit!" said Scrooge in a broken voice, "remove me from this place."

"I told you these were shadows of the things that have been," said the Ghost. "That they are what they are, do not blame me!"

"Remove me!" Scrooge exclaimed. "I cannot bear it!"

He turned upon the Ghost, and seeing that it looked upon him with a face, in which in some strange way there were fragments of all the faces it had shown him, wrestled with it.

"Leave me! Take me back. Haunt me no longer!"

In the struggle, if that can be called a struggle in which the Ghost with no visible resistance on its own part was undisturbed by any effort of its adversary, Scrooge observed that its light was burning high and bright; and dimly connecting that with its influence over him, he seized the extinguisher-cap, and by a sudden action pressed it down upon its head.

The Spirit dropped beneath it, so that the extinguisher covered its whole form; but though Scrooge pressed it down with all his force, he could not hide the light: which streamed from under it, in an unbroken flood upon the ground.

He was conscious of being exhausted, and overcome by an irresistible drowsiness; and, further, of being in his own bedroom. He gave the cap a parting squeeze, in which his hand relaxed; and had barely time to reel to bed, before he sank into a heavy sleep.

Original pencil-and-wash rendering by Leech for Dickens' approval: Scrooge extinguishing the Spirit of Christmas Past (1843). By permission of the Houghton Library, Harvard University.

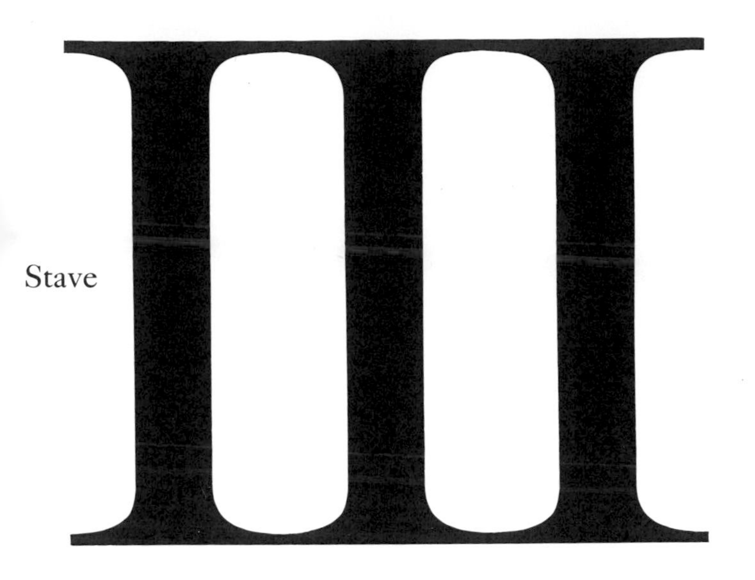

Stave III

The Second of the Three Spirits

Awaking in the middle of a prodigiously tough snore, and sitting up in bed to get his thoughts together, Scrooge had no occasion to be told that the bell was again upon the stroke of One. He felt that he was restored to consciousness in the right nick of time, for the especial purpose of holding a conference with the second messenger despatched to him through Jacob Marley's intervention. But, finding that he turned uncomfortably cold when he began to wonder which of his curtains this new spectre would draw back, he put them every one aside with his own hands; and lying down again, established a sharp look-out all round the bed. For he wished to challenge the Spirit on the moment of its appearance, and did not wish to be taken by surprise and made nervous.

Gentlemen of the free-and-easy sort, who plume themselves on being acquainted with a move or two, and being usually equal to the time-of-day, express the wide range of their capacity for adventure by observing that they are good for anything from pitch-and-toss to manslaughter; between which opposite extremes, no doubt, there lies a tolerably wide and comprehensive range of subjects. Without venturing for Scrooge quite as hardily as this, I don't mind calling on you to believe that he was ready for a good broad field of strange appearances, and that nothing between a baby and a rhinoceros would have astonished him very much.

Now, being prepared for almost anything, he was not by any means prepared for nothing; and, consequently, when the Bell struck One, and no shape appeared, he was taken with a violent fit of trembling. Five minutes, ten minutes, a quarter of an hour went by, yet nothing came. All this time, he lay upon his bed, the very core and centre of a blaze of ruddy light, which streamed upon it when the clock proclaimed the hour; and which being only light, was more alarming than a dozen ghosts, as he was powerless to make out what it meant, or would be at; and was sometimes apprehensive that he might be at that very moment an interesting case of spontaneous combustion, without having the consolation of knowing it. At last, however, he began to think–as you or I would have thought at first; for it is always the person not in the predicament who knows what ought to have been done in it, and would unquestionably have done it too–at last, I say, he began to think that the source and secret of this ghostly light might be in the adjoining room: from whence, on further tracing it, it seemed to shine. This idea taking full possession of his mind, he got up softly and shuffled in his slippers to the door.

The moment Scrooge's hand was on the lock, a strange voice called him by his name, and bade him enter. He obeyed.

It was his own room. There was no doubt about that. But it had undergone a surprising transformation. The walls and ceiling were so hung with living green, that it looked a perfect grove, from every part of which, bright gleaming berries glistened. The crisp leaves of holly, mistletoe, and ivy reflected back the light, as if so many little mirrors had been scattered there; and such a mighty blaze went roaring up the chimney, as that dull petrification of a hearth had never known in Scrooge's time, or Marley's, or for many and many a winter season gone. Heaped up on the floor, to form a kind of throne, were turkeys, geese, game, poultry, brawn, great joints of meat, sucking-pigs, long wreaths of sau-

"Ghost of Christmas Present," original color illustration by John Leech (1843). Courtesy Beinecke Rare Book and Manuscript Library, Yale University.

sages, mince-pies, plum-puddings, barrels of oysters, red-hot chestnuts, cherry-cheeked apples, juicy oranges, luscious pears, immense twelfth-cakes, and seething bowls of punch, that made the chamber dim with their delicious steam. In easy state upon this couch, there sat a jolly Giant, glorious to see; who bore a glowing torch, in shape not unlike Plenty's horn, and held it up, high up, to shed its light on Scrooge, as he came peeping round the door.

"Come in!" exclaimed the Ghost. "Come in! and know me better, man!"

Scrooge entered timidly, and hung his head before this Spirit. He was not the dogged Scrooge he had been; and though the Spirit's eyes were clear and kind, he did not like to meet them.

"I am the Ghost of Christmas Present," said the Spirit. "Look upon me!"

Scrooge reverently did so. It was clothed in one simple deep green robe, or mantle, bordered with white fur. This garment hung so loosely on the figure, that its capacious breast was bare, as if disdaining to be warded or concealed by any artifice. Its feet, observable beneath the ample folds of the garment, were also bare; and on its head it wore no other covering than a holly wreath, set here and there with shining icicles. Its dark brown curls were long and free: free as its genial face, its sparkling eye, its open hand, its cheery voice, its unconstrained demeanour, and its joyful air. Girded round its middle was an antique scabbard; but no sword was in it, and the ancient sheath was eaten up with rust.

"You have never seen the like of me before!" exclaimed the Spirit.

"Never," Scrooge made answer to it.

"Have never walked forth with the younger members of my family; meaning (for I am very young) my elder brothers born in these later years?" pursued the Phantom.

"I don't think I have," said Scrooge. "I am afraid I have not. Have you had many brothers, Spirit?"

"More than eighteen hundred," said the Ghost.

"A tremendous family to provide for!" muttered Scrooge.

The Ghost of Christmas Present rose.

"Spirit," said Scrooge submissively, "conduct me where you will. I went forth last night on compulsion, and I learnt a lesson which is working now. To-night, if you have aught to teach me, let me profit by it."

"Touch my robe!"

Scrooge did as he was told, and held it fast.

Holly, mistletoe, red berries, ivy, turkeys, geese, game, poultry, brawn, meat, pigs, sausages, oysters, pies, puddings, fruit, and punch, all vanished instantly. So did the room, the fire, the ruddy glow, the hour of night, and they stood in the city streets on Christmas morning, where (for the weather was severe) the people made a rough, but brisk and not unpleasant kind of music, in scraping the snow from the pavement in front of their dwellings, and from the tops of their houses: whence it was mad delight to the boys to see it come plumping down into the road below, and splitting into artificial little snowstorms.

The house fronts looked black enough, and the windows blacker, contrasting with the smooth white sheet of snow upon the roofs, and with the dirtier snow upon the ground; which last deposit had been ploughed up in deep furrows by the heavy wheels of carts and waggons; furrows that crossed and re-crossed each other hundreds of times where the great streets branched off, and made intricate channels, hard to trace, in the thick yellow mud and icy water. The sky was gloomy, and the shortest streets were choked up with a dingy mist, half thawed, half frozen, whose heavier particles descended in a shower of sooty atoms, as if all the chimneys in Great Britain had, by one consent, caught fire, and were blazing away to their dear hearts' content. There was nothing very cheerful in the climate or the town, and yet was there an air of cheerfulness abroad that the clearest summer air and brightest summer sun might have endeavoured to diffuse in vain.

For the people who were shovelling away on the housetops were jovial and full of glee; calling out to one another from the parapets, and now and then exchanging a facetious snowball–better-natured missile far than many a wordy jest–laughing heartily if it went right, and not less heartily if it went wrong. The poulterers' shops were still half open, and the fruiterers' were radiant in their glory. There were great round, pot-bellied baskets of chestnuts, shaped like the waistcoats of jolly old gentlemen, lolling at the doors, and tumbling out into the street in their apoplectic opulence. There were ruddy, brown-faced, broad-girthed Spanish Onions, shining in the fatness of their growth like Spanish Friars; and winking from their shelves in wanton slyness at the girls as they went by, and glanced demurely at the hung-up mistletoe. There were pears and apples, clustered high in blooming pyramids; there were bunches of grapes, made in the shopkeepers' benevolence to dangle from conspicuous hooks, that people's mouths might water gratis as they passed; there were piles of filberts, mossy and brown, recalling, in their fragrance, ancient walks among the woods, and pleasant shufflings ankle deep through withered leaves; there were Norfolk Biffins, squab and swarthy, setting off the yellow of the oranges and lemons, and, in the great compactness of their juicy persons, urgently entreating and beseeching to be carried home in paper bags and eaten after dinner. The very gold and silver fish, set forth among these choice fruits in a bowl, though members of a dull and stagnant-blooded race, appeared to know that there was something going on; and, to a fish, went gasping round and round their little world in slow and passionless excitement.

The Grocers'! oh the Grocers'! nearly closed, with perhaps two shutters down, or one; but through those gaps such glimpses! It was not alone that the scales descending on the counter made a merry sound, or that the twine and roller parted company so briskly, or that the canisters were rattled up and down like juggling tricks, or even that the blended scents of tea and coffee were so grateful to the nose, or even that the raisins were so plentiful and rare, the almonds so extremely white, the sticks of cinnamon so long and straight, the other spices so delicious, the candied fruits so caked and spotted with molten sugar as to make the coldest lookers-on feel faint and subsequently bilious. Nor was it that the figs were moist and pulpy, or that the French plums blushed in modest tartness from their highly-decorated boxes, or that everything was good to eat and in its Christmas dress: but the customers were all so hurried and so eager in the hopeful promise of the day, that they tumbled up against each other at the door, clashing their wicker baskets wildly, and left their purchases upon the counter, and came running back to fetch them, and committed hundreds of the like mistakes in the best humour possible; while the Grocer and his people were so frank and fresh that the polished hearts with which they fastened their aprons behind might have been their own, worn outside for general inspection, and for Christmas daws to peck at if they chose.

But soon the steeples called good people all, to church and chapel, and away they came, flocking through the streets in their best clothes, and with their gayest faces. And at the same time there emerged from scores of bye streets, lanes, and nameless turnings, innumerable people, carrying their dinners to the bakers' shops. The sight of these poor revellers appeared to interest the Spirit very much, for he stood with Scrooge beside him in a baker's doorway, and taking off the covers as their bearers passed, sprinkled incense on their dinners from his torch. And it was a very uncommon kind of torch, for once or twice when there were angry words between some dinner-carriers who had jostled each other, he shed a few drops of water on them from it, and their good humour was restored directly. For they said, it was a shame to quarrel upon Christmas Day. And so it was! God love it, so it was!

In time the bells ceased, and the bakers' were shut up; and yet there was a genial shadowing forth of all these dinners and the progress of their cooking, in the thawed blotch of wet above each baker's oven; where the pavement smoked as if its stones were cooking too.

"Is there a peculiar flavour in what you sprinkle from your torch?" asked Scrooge.

"There is. My own."

"Would it apply to any kind of dinner on this day?" asked Scrooge.

"To any kindly given. To a poor one most."

"Why to a poor one most?" asked Scrooge.

"Because it needs it most."

"Spirit," said Scrooge, after a moment's thought, "I wonder you, of all the beings in the many worlds about us, should desire to cramp these people's opportunities of innocent enjoyment."

"I!" cried the Spirit.

"You would deprive them of their means of dining every seventh day, often the only day on which they can be said to dine at all," said Scrooge. "Wouldn't you?"

"I!" cried the Spirit.

"You seek to close these places on the Seventh Day?" said Scrooge. "And it comes to the same thing."

"*I* seek!" exclaimed the Spirit.

"Forgive me if I am wrong. It has been done in your name, or at least in that of your family," said Scrooge.

"There are some upon this earth of yours," returned the Spirit, "who lay claim to know us, and who do their deeds of passion, pride, ill-will, hatred, envy, bigotry, and selfishness in our name, who are as strange to us and all our kith and kin, as if they had never lived. Remember that, and charge their doings on themselves, not us."

Scrooge promised that he would; and they went on, invisible, as they had been before, into the suburbs of the town. It was a remarkable quality of the Ghost (which Scrooge had observed at the baker's) that notwithstanding his gigantic size, he could accommodate himself to any place with ease; and that he stood beneath a low roof quite as gracefully and like a supernatural creature, as it was possible he could have done in any lofty hall.

And perhaps it was the pleasure the good Spirit had in showing off this power of his, or else it was his own kind, generous, hearty nature, and his sympathy with all poor men, that led him straight to Scrooge's clerk's; for there he went, and took Scrooge with him, holding to his robe; and on the threshold of the door the Spirit smiled, and stopped to bless Bob Cratchit's dwelling with the sprinkling of his torch. Think of that! Bob had but fifteen "Bob" a-week himself; he pocketed on Saturdays but fifteen copies of his Christian name; and yet the Ghost of Christmas Present blessed his four-roomed house!

Then up rose Mrs. Cratchit, Cratchit's wife, dressed out but poorly in a twice-turned gown, but brave in ribbons, which are cheap and make a goodly show for sixpence; and she laid the cloth, assisted by Belinda Cratchit, second of her daughters, also brave in ribbons; while Master Peter Cratchit plunged a fork into the saucepan of potatoes, and getting the corners of his monstrous shirt-collar (Bob's private property, conferred upon his son and heir in honour of the day) into his mouth, rejoiced to find himself so gallantly attired, and yearned to show his linen in the fashionable Parks. And now two smaller Cratchits, boy and girl, came tearing in, screaming that outside the baker's they had smelt the goose, and known it for their own; and basking in luxurious thoughts of sage and onion, these young Cratchits danced about the table, and exalted Master Peter Cratchit to the skies, while he (not proud, although his collars nearly choked him) blew the fire, until the slow potatoes bubbling up, knocked loudly at the saucepan-lid to be let out and peeled.

"What has ever got your precious father then," said Mrs. Cratchit. "And your brother, Tiny Tim; and Martha warn't as late last Christmas Day by half-an-hour!"

"Here's Martha, mother!" said a girl, appearing as she spoke.

"Here's Martha, mother!" cried the two young Cratchits. "Hurrah! There's *such* a goose, Martha!"

"Why, bless your heart alive, my dear, how late you are!" said Mrs. Cratchit, kissing her a dozen times, and taking off her shawl and bonnet for her, with officious zeal.

"We'd a deal of work to finish up last night," replied the girl, "and had to clear away this morning, mother!"

"Well! Never mind so long as you are come," said Mrs. Cratchit. "Sit ye down before the fire, my dear, and have a warm, Lord bless ye!"

"No no! There's father coming," cried the two young Cratchits, who were everywhere at once. "Hide Martha, hide!"

So Martha hid herself, and in came little Bob, the father, with at least three feet of comforter exclusive of the fringe, hanging down before him; and his thread-bare clothes darned up and brushed, to look seasonable; and Tiny Tim upon his shoulder. Alas for Tiny Tim, he bore a little crutch, and had his limbs supported by an iron frame!

"Why, where's our Martha?" cried Bob Cratchit looking round.

"Not coming," said Mrs. Cratchit.

"Not coming!" said Bob, with a sudden declension in his high spirits; for he had been Tim's blood horse all the way from church, and had come home rampant. "Not coming upon Christmas Day!"

Martha didn't like to see him disappointed, if it were only in joke; so she came out prematurely from behind the closet door, and ran into his arms, while the two young Cratchits hustled Tiny Tim, and bore him off into the wash-house, that he might hear the pudding singing in the copper.

"And how did little Tim behave?" asked Mrs. Cratchit, when she had rallied Bob on his credulity and Bob had hugged his daughter to his heart's content.

"As good as gold," said Bob, "and better. Somehow he gets thoughtful sitting by himself so much, and thinks the strangest things you ever heard. He told me, coming home, that he hoped the people saw him in the church, because he was a cripple, and it might be pleasant to them to remember upon Christmas Day, who made lame beggars walk and blind men see."

Bob's voice was tremulous when he told them this, and trembled more when he said that Tiny Tim was growing strong and hearty.

His active little crutch was heard upon the floor, and back came Tiny Tim before another word was spoken, escorted by his brother and sister to his stool before the fire; and while Bob, turning up his cuffs–as if, poor fellow, they were capable of being made more shabby–compounded some hot mixture in a jug with gin and lemons, and stirred it round and round and put it on the hob to simmer; Master Peter, and the two ubiquitous young Cratchits went to fetch the goose, with which they soon returned in high procession.

Such a bustle ensued that you might have thought a goose the rarest of all birds; a feathered phenomenon, to which a black swan was a matter of course; and in truth it was something very like it in that house. Mrs. Cratchit made the gravy (ready beforehand in a little saucepan) hissing hot; Master Peter mashed the potatoes with incredible vigour; Miss Belinda sweetened up the apple-sauce; Martha dusted the hot plates; Bob took Tiny Tim beside him in a tiny corner at the table; the two young Cratchits set chairs for everybody, not forgetting themselves, and mounting guard upon their posts, crammed spoons into their mouths, lest they should shriek for goose before their turn came to be helped. At last the dishes were set on, and grace was said. It was succeeded by a breathless pause, as Mrs. Cratchit, looking slowly all along the carving-knife, prepared to plunge it in the breast; but when she did, and when the long expected gush of stuffing issued forth, one murmur of delight arose all round the board, and even Tiny Tim, excited by the two young Cratchits, beat on the table with the handle of his knife, and feebly cried Hurrah!

There never was such a goose. Bob said he didn't believe there ever was such a goose cooked. Its tenderness and flavour, size and cheapness, were the themes of universal admiration. Eked out by the apple-sauce and mashed potatoes, it was a sufficient dinner for the whole family; indeed, as Mrs. Cratchit said with great delight (surveying one small atom of a bone upon the dish), they hadn't ate it all at last! Yet every one had had enough, and the youngest Cratchits in particular, were steeped in sage and onion to the eyebrows! But now, the plates being changed by Miss Belinda, Mrs. Cratchit left the room alone–too nervous to bear witnesses–to take the pudding up, and bring it in.

Suppose it should not be done enough! Suppose it should break in turning out! Suppose somebody should have got over the wall of the back-yard, and stolen it, while they were merry with the goose: a supposition at which the two young Cratchits became livid! All sorts of horrors were supposed.

Hallo! A great deal of steam! The pudding was out of the copper. A smell like a washing-day! That was the cloth. A smell like an eating-house, and a pastry cook's next door to each other, with a laundress's next door to that! That was the pudding. In half a minute Mrs. Cratchit entered: flushed, but smiling proudly: with the pudding, like a speckled cannon-ball, so hard and firm, blazing in half of half-a-quartern of ignited brandy, and bedight with Christmas holly stuck into the top.

Oh, a wonderful pudding! Bob Cratchit said, and calmly too, that he regarded it as the greatest success achieved by Mrs. Cratchit since their marriage. Mrs. Cratchit said that now the weight was off her mind, she would confess she had had her doubts about the quantity of flour. Everybody had something to say about it, but nobody said or thought it was at all a small pudding for a large family. It would have been flat heresy to do so. Any Cratchit would have blushed to hint at such a thing.

At last the dinner was all done, the cloth was cleared, the hearth swept, and the fire made up. The compound in the jug being tasted, and considered perfect, apples and oranges were put upon the table, and a shovel-full of chestnuts on the fire. Then all the Cratchit family drew round the hearth, in what Bob Cratchit called a circle, meaning half a one; and at Bob Cratchit's elbow stood the family display of glass; two tumblers, and a custard-cup without a handle.

These held the hot stuff from the jug, however, as well as golden goblets would have done; and Bob served it out with beaming looks, while the chestnuts on the fire sputtered and crackled noisily. Then Bob proposed:

"A Merry Christmas to us all, my dears. God bless us!"

Which all the family re-echoed.

"God bless us every one!" said Tiny Tim, the last of all.

He sat very close to his father's side, upon his little stool. Bob held his withered little hand in his, as if he loved the child, and wished to keep him by his side, and dreaded that he might be taken from him.

"Spirit," said Scrooge, with an interest he had never felt before, "tell me if Tiny Tim will live."

"I see a vacant seat," replied the Ghost, "in the poor chimney corner, and a crutch without an owner, carefully preserved. If these shadows remain unaltered by the Future, the child will die."

"No, no," said Scrooge. "Oh no, kind Spirit! say he will be spared."

"If these shadows remain unaltered by the Future, none other of my race," returned the Ghost, "will find him here. What then? If he be like to die, he had better do it, and decrease the surplus population."

Scrooge hung his head to hear his own words quoted by the Spirit, and was overcome with penitence and grief.

"Man," said the Ghost, "if man you be in heart, not adamant, forbear that wicked cant until you have discovered What the surplus is, and Where it is. Will you decide what men shall live, what men shall die? It may be, that in the sight of Heaven, you are more worthless and less fit to live than millions like this poor man's child. Oh God! to hear the Insect on the leaf pronouncing on the too much life among his hungry brothers in the dust!"

Scrooge bent before the Ghost's rebuke, and trembling cast his eyes upon the ground. But he raised them speedily, on hearing his own name.

"Mr. Scrooge!" said Bob; "I'll give you Mr. Scrooge, the Founder of the Feast!"

"The Founder of the Feast indeed!" cried Mrs. Cratchit, reddening. "I wish I had him here. I'd give him a piece of my mind to feast upon, and I hope he'd have a good appetite for it."

"My dear," said Bob, "the children; Christmas Day."

"It should be Christmas Day, I am sure," said she, "on which one drinks the health of such an odious, stingy, hard, unfeeling man as Mr. Scrooge. You know he is, Robert! Nobody knows it better than you do, poor fellow!"

"My dear," was Bob's mild answer, "Christmas Day."

"I'll drink his health for your sake and the Day's," said Mrs. Cratchit, "not for his. Long life to him! A merry Christmas and a happy new year!–he'll be very merry and very happy, I have no doubt!"

The children drank the toast after her. It was the first of their proceedings which had no heartiness in it. Tiny Tim drank it last of all, but he didn't care twopence for it. Scrooge was the Ogre of the family. The mention of his name cast a dark shadow on the party, which was not dispelled for full five minutes.

After it had passed away, they were ten times merrier than before, from the mere relief of Scrooge the Baleful being done with. Bob Cratchit told them how he had a situation in his eye for Master Peter, which would bring in, if obtained, full five-and-sixpence weekly. The two young Cratchits laughed tremendously at the idea of Peter's being a man of business; and Peter himself looked thoughtfully at the fire from between his collars, as if he were deliberating what particular investments he should favour when he came into the receipt of that bewildering income. Martha, who was a poor apprentice at a milliner's, then told them what kind of work she had to do, and how many hours she worked at a stretch, and how she meant to lie a-bed to-morrow morning for a good long rest; to-morrow being a holiday she passed at home. Also how she had seen a countess and a lord some days before, and how the lord "was much about as tall as Peter"; at which Peter pulled up his collars so high that you couldn't have seen his head if you had been there. All this time the chestnuts and the jug went round and round; and bye and bye they had a song, about a lost child travelling in the snow, from Tiny Tim; who had a plaintive little voice, and sang it very well indeed.

There was nothing of high mark in this. They were not a handsome family; they were not well dressed; their shoes were far from being water-proof; their clothes were scanty; and Peter might have known, and very likely did, the inside of a pawnbroker's. But they were happy, grateful, pleased with one another, and contented with the time; and when they faded, and looked happier yet in the bright sprinklings of the Spirit's torch at parting, Scrooge had his eye upon them, and especially on Tiny Tim, until the last.

By this time it was getting dark, and snowing pretty heavily; and as Scrooge and the Spirit went along the streets, the brightness of the roaring fires in kitchens, parlours, and all sorts of rooms, was wonderful. Here, the flickering of the blaze showed preparations for a cosy dinner, with hot plates baking through and through before the fire, and deep red curtains, ready to be drawn, to shut out cold and darkness. There, all the children of the house were running out into the snow to meet their married sisters, brothers, cousins, uncles, aunts, and be the first to greet them. Here, again, were shadows on the window-blind of guests assembling; and there a group of handsome girls, all hooded and fur-booted, and all chattering at once, tripped lightly off to some near neighbour's house; where, woe upon the single man who saw them enter–artful witches: well they knew it–in a glow!

But if you had judged from the numbers of people on their way to friendly gatherings, you might have thought that no one was at home to give them welcome when they got there, instead of every house expecting company, and piling up its fires half-chimney high. Blessings on it, how the Ghost exulted! How it bared its breadth of breast, and opened its capacious palm, and floated on, outpouring, with a generous hand, its bright and harmless mirth on everything within its reach! The very lamplighter, who ran on before dotting the dusky street with specks of light, and who was dressed to spend the evening somewhere, laughed out loudly as the Spirit passed: though little kenned the lamplighter that he had any company but Christmas!

And now, without a word of warning from the Ghost, they stood upon a bleak and desert moor, where monstrous masses of rude stone were cast about, as though it were the burial-place of giants; and water spread itself wheresoever it listed–or would have done so, but for the frost that held it prisoner; and nothing grew but moss and furze, and coarse, rank grass. Down in the west the setting sun had left a streak of fiery red, which glared upon the desolation for an instant, like a sullen eye, and frowning lower, lower, lower yet, was lost in the thick gloom of darkest night.

"What place is this?" asked Scrooge.

"A place where Miners live, who labour in the bowels of the earth," returned the Spirit. "But they know me. See!"

A light shone from the window of a hut, and swiftly they advanced towards it. Passing through the wall of mud and stone, they found a cheerful company assembled round a glowing fire. An old, old man and woman, with their children and their children's children, and another generation beyond that, all decked out gaily in their holiday attire. The old man, in a voice that seldom rose above the howling of the wind upon the barren waste, was singing them a Christmas song; it had been a very old song when he was a boy; and from time to time they all joined in the chorus. So surely as they raised their voices, the old man got quite blithe and loud; and so surely as they stopped, his vigour sank again.

The Spirit did not tarry here, but bade Scrooge hold his robe, and passing on above the moor, sped whither? Not to sea? To sea. To Scrooge's horror, looking back, he saw the last of the land, a frightful range of rocks, behind them; and his ears were deafened by the thundering of water, as it rolled, and roared, and raged among the dreadful caverns it had worn, and fiercely tried to undermine the earth.

Built upon a dismal reef of sunken rocks, some league or so from shore, on which the waters chafed and dashed, the wild year through, there stood a solitary lighthouse. Great heaps of sea-weed clung to its base, and storm-birds–born of the wind one might suppose, as sea-weed of the water–rose and fell about it, like the waves they skimmed.

But even here, two men who watched the light had made a fire, that through the loophole in the thick stone wall shed out a ray of brightness on the awful sea. Joining their horny hands over the rough table at which they sat, they wished each other Merry Christmas in their can of grog; and one of them: the elder, too, with his face all damaged and scarred with hard weather, as the figure-head of an old ship might be: struck up a sturdy song that was like a Gale in itself.

Again the Ghost sped on, above the black and heaving sea–on, on–until, being far away, as he told Scrooge, from any shore, they lighted on a ship. They stood beside the helmsman at the wheel, the look-out in the bow, the officers who had the watch; dark, ghostly figures in their several stations; but every man among them hummed a Christmas tune, or had a Christmas thought, or spoke below his breath to his companion of some bygone Christmas Day, with homeward hopes belonging to it. And every man on board, waking or sleeping, good or bad, had had a kinder word for another on that day than on any day in the year; and had shared to some extent in its festivities; and had remembered those he cared for at a distance, and had known that they delighted to remember him.

It was a great surprise to Scrooge, while listening to the moaning of the wind, and thinking what a solemn thing it was to move on through the lonely darkness over an unknown abyss, whose depths were secrets as profound as Death: it was a great surprise to Scrooge, while thus engaged, to hear a hearty laugh. It was a much greater surprise to Scrooge to recognise it as his own nephew's, and to find himself in a bright, dry, gleaming room, with the Spirit standing smiling by his side, and looking at that same nephew with approving affability!

"Ha, ha!" laughed Scrooge's nephew. "Ha, ha, ha!"

If you should happen, by any unlikely chance, to know a man more blest in a laugh than Scrooge's nephew, all I can say is, I should like to know him too. Introduce him to me, and I'll cultivate his acquaintance.

It is a fair, even-handed, noble adjustment of things, that while there is infection in disease and sorrow, there is nothing in the world so irresistibly contagious as laughter and good-humour. When Scrooge's nephew laughed in this way: holding his sides, rolling his head, and twisting his face into the most extravagant contortions: Scrooge's niece, by marriage, laughed as heartily as he. And their assembled friends being not a bit behindhand, roared out, lustily.

"Ha, ha! Ha, ha, ha, ha!"

"He said that Christmas was a humbug, as I live!" cried Scrooge's nephew. "He believed it too!"

"More shame for him, Fred!" said Scrooge's niece, indignantly. Bless those women; they never do anything by halves. They are always in earnest.

She was very pretty: exceedingly pretty. With a dimpled, surprised-looking, capital face; a ripe little mouth, that seemed made to be kissed–as no doubt it was; all kinds of good little dots about her chin, that melted into one another when she laughed; and the sunniest pair of eyes you ever saw in any little creature's head. Altogether she was what you would have called provoking, you know; but satisfactory too. Oh, perfectly satisfactory!

"He's a comical old fellow," said Scrooge's nephew, "that's the truth: and not so pleasant as he might be. However, his offences carry their own punishment, and I have nothing to say against him."

"I'm sure he is very rich, Fred," hinted Scrooge's niece. "At least you always tell *me* so."

"What of that, my dear!" said Scrooge's nephew. "His wealth is of no use to him. He don't do any good with it. He don't make himself comfortable with it. He hasn't the satisfaction of thinking–ha, ha, ha!–that he is ever going to benefit Us with it."

"I have no patience with him," observed Scrooge's niece. Scrooge's niece's sisters, and all the other ladies, expressed the same opinion.

"Oh, I have!" said Scrooge's nephew. "I am sorry for him; I couldn't be angry with him if I tried. Who suffers by his ill whims! Himself, always. Here, he takes it into his head to dislike us, and he won't come and dine with us. What's the consequence? He don't lose much of a dinner."

"Indeed, I think he loses a very good dinner," interrupted Scrooge's niece. Everybody else said the same, and they must be allowed to have been competent judges, because they had just had dinner; and, with the dessert upon the table, were clustered round the fire, by lamplight.

"Well! I'm very glad to hear it," said Scrooge's nephew, "because I haven't great faith in these young housekeepers. What do *you* say, Topper?"

Topper had clearly got his eye upon one of Scrooge's niece's sisters, for he answered that a bachelor was a wretched outcast, who had no right to express an opinion on the subject. Whereat Scrooge's niece's sister–the plump one with the lace tucker: not the one with the roses–blushed.

"Do go on, Fred," said Scrooge's niece, clapping her hands. "He never finishes what he begins to say! He is such a ridiculous fellow!"

Scrooge's nephew revelled in another laugh, and as it was impossible to keep the infection off; though the plump sister tried hard to do it with aromatic vinegar; his example was unanimously followed.

"I was going to say," said Scrooge's nephew, "that the consequence of his taking a dislike to us, and not making merry with us, is, as I think, that he loses some pleasant moments, which could do him no harm. I am sure he loses pleasanter companions than he can find in his own thoughts, either in his mouldy old office, or his dusty chambers. I mean to give him the same chance every year, whether he likes it or not, for I pity him. He may rail at Christmas till he dies, but he can't help thinking better of it–I defy him–if he finds me going there, in good temper, year after year, and saying Uncle Scrooge, how are you? If it only puts him in the vein to leave his poor clerk fifty pounds, *that's* something; and I think I shook him, yesterday."

It was their turn to laugh now, at the notion of his shaking Scrooge. But being thoroughly good-natured, and not much caring what they laughed at, so that they laughed at any rate, he encouraged them in their merriment, and passed the bottle, joyously.

After tea, they had some music. For they were a

musical family, and knew what they were about, when they sung a Glee or Catch, I can assure you: especially Topper, who could growl away in the bass like a good one, and never swell the large veins in his forehead, or get red in the face over it. Scrooge's niece played well upon the harp; and played among other tunes a simple little air (a mere nothing: you might learn to whistle it in two minutes), which had been familiar to the child who fetched Scrooge from the boarding-school, as he had been reminded by the Ghost of Christmas Past. When this strain of music sounded, all the things that Ghost had shown him, came upon his mind; he softened more and more; and thought that if he could have listened to it often, years ago, he might have cultivated the kindnesses of life for his own happiness with his own hands, without resorting to the sexton's spade that buried Jacob Marley.

But they didn't devote the whole evening to music. After a while they played at forfeits; for it is good to be children sometimes, and never better than at Christmas, when its mighty Founder was a child himself. Stop! There was first a game at blind-man's buff. Of course there was. And I no more believe Topper was really blind than I believe he had eyes in his boots. My opinion is, that it was a done thing between him and Scrooge's nephew; and that the Ghost of Christmas Present knew it. The way he went after that plump sister in the lace tucker, was an outrage on the credulity of human nature. Knocking down the fire-irons, tumbling over the chairs, bumping against the piano, smothering himself among the curtains, wherever she went, there went he. He always knew where the plump sister was. He wouldn't catch anybody else. If you had fallen up against him, as some of them did, and stood there; he would have made a feint of endeavouring to seize you, which would have been an affront to your understanding; and would instantly have sidled off in the direction of the plump sister. She often cried out that it wasn't fair; and it really was not. But when at last, he caught her; when, in spite of all her silken rustlings, and her rapid flutterings past him, he got her into a corner whence there was no escape; then his conduct was the most execrable. For his pretending not to know her; his pretending that it was necessary to touch her head-dress, and further to assure himself of her identity by pressing a certain ring upon her finger, and a certain chain about her neck; was vile, monstrous! No doubt she told him her opinion of it, when, another blind-man being in office, they were so very confidential together, behind the curtains.

Scrooge's niece was not one of the blind-man's buff party, but was made comfortable with a large chair and a footstool, in a snug corner, where the Ghost and Scrooge were close behind her. But she joined in the forfeits, and loved her love to admiration with all the letters of the alphabet. Likewise at the game of How, When, and Where, she was very great, and to the secret joy of Scrooge's nephew, beat her sisters hollow: though they were sharp girls too, as Topper could have told you. There might have been twenty people there, young and old, but they all played, and so did Scrooge; for wholly forgetting in the interest he had in what was going on, that his voice made no sound in their ears, he sometimes came out with his guess quite loud, and very often guessed quite right, too; for the sharpest needle, best Whitechapel, warranted not to cut in the eye, was not sharper than Scrooge: blunt as he took it in his head to be.

The Ghost was greatly pleased to find him in this mood, and looked upon him with such favour that he begged like a boy to be allowed to stay until the guests departed. But this the Spirit said could not be done.

"Here's a new game," said Scrooge. "One half hour, Spirit, only one!"

It was a Game called Yes and No, where Scrooge's nephew had to think of something, and the rest must find out what; he only answering to their questions yes or no as the case was. The brisk fire of questioning to which he was exposed, elicited from him that he was thinking of an animal, a live animal, rather a disagreeable animal, a savage animal, an animal that growled and grunted sometimes, and talked sometimes, and lived in London, and walked about the streets, and wasn't made a show of, and wasn't led by anybody, and didn't live in a menagerie, and was never killed in a market, and was not a horse, or an ass, or a cow, or a bull, or a tiger, or a dog, or a pig, or a cat, or a bear. At every fresh question that was put to him, this nephew burst into a fresh roar of laughter; and was so inexpressibly tickled, that he was obliged to get up off the sofa and stamp. At last the plump sister, falling into a similar state, cried out:

"I have found it out! I know what it is, Fred! I know what it is!"

"What is it?" cried Fred.

"It's your Uncle Scro-o-o-o-o-ge!"

Which it certainly was. Admiration was the universal sentiment, though some objected that the reply to "Is it a bear?" ought to have been "Yes;" inasmuch as an answer in the negative was sufficient to have diverted their thoughts from Mr. Scrooge, supposing they had ever had any tendency that way.

"He has given us plenty of merriment, I am sure," said Fred, "and it would be ungrateful not to drink his health. Here is a glass of mulled wine ready to our hand at the moment; and I say 'Uncle Scrooge!'"

"Well! Uncle Scrooge!" they cried.

"A Merry Christmas and a Happy New Year to the old man, whatever he is!" said Scrooge's nephew. "He wouldn't take it from me, but may he have it, nevertheless. Uncle Scrooge!"

Uncle Scrooge had imperceptibly become so gay and light of heart, that he would have pledged the unconscious company in return, and thanked them in an inaudible speech, if the Ghost had given him time. But the whole scene passed off in the breath of the last word spoken by his nephew; and he and the Spirit were again upon their travels.

Much they saw, and far they went, and many homes they visited, but always with a happy end. The Spirit stood beside sick beds, and they were cheerful; on foreign lands, and they were close at home; by struggling men, and they were patient in their greater hope; by poverty, and it was rich. In almshouse, hospital, and jail, in misery's every refuge, where vain man in his little brief authority had not made fast the door, and barred the Spirit out, he left his blessing, and taught Scrooge his precepts.

It was a long night, if it were only a night; but Scrooge had his doubts of this, because the Christmas Holidays appeared to be condensed into the space of time they passed together. It was strange, too, that while Scrooge remained unaltered in his outward form, the Ghost grew older, clearly older. Scrooge had observed this change, but never spoke of it, until they left a children's Twelfth Night party, when, looking at the Spirit as they stood together in an open place, he noticed that its hair was gray.

"Are spirits' lives so short?" asked Scrooge.

"My life upon this globe, is very brief," replied the Ghost. "It ends to-night."

"To-night!" cried Scrooge.

"To-night at midnight. Hark! The time is drawing near."

The chimes were ringing the three quarters past eleven at that moment.

"Forgive me if I am not justified in what I ask," said Scrooge, looking intently at the Spirit's robe, "but I see something strange, and not belonging to yourself, protruding from your skirts. Is it a foot or a claw!"

"It might be a claw, for the flesh there is upon it," was the Spirit's sorrowful reply. "Look here."

From the foldings of its robe, it brought two children; wretched, abject, frightful, hideous, miserable. They knelt down at its feet, and clung upon the outside of its garment.

"Oh, Man! look here. Look, look, down here!" exclaimed the Ghost.

They were a boy and girl. Yellow, meagre, ragged, scowling, wolfish; but prostrate, too, in their humility. Where graceful youth should have filled their features out, and touched them with its freshest tints, a stale and shrivelled hand, like that of age, had pinched, and twisted them, and pulled them into shreds. Where angels might have sat enthroned, devils lurked; and glared out menacing. No change, no degradation, no perversion of humanity, in any

Original pencil-and-wash rendering by Leech for Dickens' approval: The Spirit of Christmas Present with Ignorance and Want (1843). By permission of the Houghton Library, Harvard University.

grade, through all the mysteries of wonderful creation, has monsters half so horrible and dread.

Scrooge started back, appalled. Having them shown to him in this way, he tried to say they were fine children, but the words choked themselves, rather than be parties to a lie of such enormous magnitude.

"Spirit! are they yours?" Scrooge could say no more.

"They are Man's," said the Spirit, looking down upon them. "And they cling to me, appealing from their fathers. This boy is Ignorance. This girl is Want. Beware them both, and all of their degree, but most of all beware this boy, for on his brow I see that written which is Doom, unless the writing be erased. Deny it!" cried the Spirit, stretching out its hand towards the city. "Slander those who tell it ye! Admit it for your factious purposes, and make it worse. And bide the end!"

"Have they no refuge or resource?" cried Scrooge.

"Are there no prisons?" said the Spirit, turning on him for the last time with his own words. "Are there no workhouses?"

The bell struck twelve.

Scrooge looked about him for the Ghost, and saw it not. As the last stroke ceased to vibrate, he remembered the prediction of old Jacob Marley, and lifting up his eyes, beheld a solemn Phantom, draped and hooded, coming, like a mist along the ground, towards him.

Stave IV The Last of the Spirits

The Phantom slowly, gravely, silently, approached. When it came near him, Scrooge bent down upon his knee; for in the very air through which this Spirit moved it seemed to scatter gloom and mystery.

It was shrouded in a deep black garment, which concealed its head, its face, its form, and left nothing of it visible save one outstretched hand. But for this it would have been difficult to detach its figure from the night, and separate it from the darkness by which it was surrounded.

He felt that it was tall and stately when it came beside him, and that its mysterious presence filled him with a solemn dread. He knew no more, for the Spirit neither spoke nor moved.

"I am in the presence of the Ghost of Christmas Yet To Come?" said Scrooge.

The Spirit answered not, but pointed onward with its hand.

"You are about to show me shadows of the things that have not happened, but will happen in the time before us," Scrooge pursued. "Is that so, Spirit?"

The upper portion of the garment was contracted for an instant in its folds, as if the Spirit had inclined its head. That was the only answer he received.

Although well used to ghostly company by this time, Scrooge feared the silent shape so much that his legs trembled beneath him, and he found that he could hardly stand when he prepared to follow it. The Spirit paused a moment, as observing his condition, and giving him time to recover.

But Scrooge was all the worse for this. It thrilled him with a vague uncertain horror, to know that behind the dusky shroud, there were ghostly eyes intently fixed upon him, while he, though he stretched his own to the utmost, could see nothing but a spectral hand and one great heap of black.

"Ghost of the Future!" he exclaimed, "I fear you more than any Spectre I have seen. But as I know your purpose is to do me good, and as I hope to live to be another man from what I was, I am prepared to bear you company, and do it with a thankful heart. Will you not speak to me?"

It gave him no reply. The hand was pointed straight before them.

"Lead on!" said Scrooge. "Lead on! The night is waning fast, and it is precious time to me, I know. Lead on, Spirit!"

The Phantom moved away as it had come towards him. Scrooge followed in the shadow of its dress, which bore him up, he thought, and carried him along.

They scarcely seemed to enter the city; for the city rather seemed to spring up about them, and encompass them of its own act. But there they were, in the heart of it; on 'Change, amongst the merchants; who hurried up and down, and chinked the money in their pockets, and conversed in groups, and looked at their watches, and trifled thoughtfully with their great gold seals; and so forth, as Scrooge had seen them often.

The Spirit stopped beside one little knot of business men. Observing that the hand was pointed to them, Scrooge advanced to listen to their talk.

"No," said a great fat man with a monstrous chin, "I don't know much about it, either way. I only know he's dead."

"When did he die?" inquired another.

"Last night, I believe."

"Why, what was the matter with him?" asked a third, taking a vast quantity of snuff out of a very large snuff-box. "I thought he'd never die."

"God knows," said the first, with a yawn.

"What has he done with his money?" asked a red-faced gentleman with a pendulous excrescence on the end of his nose, that shook like the gills of a turkey-cock.

"I haven't heard," said the man with the large chin, yawning again. "Left it to his Company, perhaps. He hasn't left it to *me*. That's all I know."

This pleasantry was received with a general laugh.

"It's likely to be a very cheap funeral," said the same speaker; "for upon my life I don't know of anybody to go to it. Suppose we make up a party and volunteer?"

"I don't mind going if a lunch is provided," observed the gentleman with the excrescence on his nose. "But I must be fed, if I make one."

Another laugh.

"Well, I am the most disinterested among you, after all," said the first speaker, "for I never wear black gloves, and I never eat lunch. But I'll offer to go, if anybody else will. When I come to think of it, I'm not at all sure that I wasn't his most particular friend; for we used to stop and speak whenever we met. Bye, bye!"

Speakers and listeners strolled away, and mixed with other groups. Scrooge knew the men, and looked towards the Spirit for an explanation.

The Phantom glided on into a street. Its finger pointed to two persons meeting. Scrooge listened again, thinking that the explanation might lie here.

He knew these men, also, perfectly. They were men of business: very wealthy, and of great importance. He had made a point always of standing well in their esteem: in a business point of view, that is; strictly in a business point of view.

"How are you?" said one.

"How are you?" returned the other.

"Well!" said the first. "Old Scratch has got his own at last, hey?"

"So I am told," returned the second. "Cold, isn't it?"

"Seasonable for Christmas time. You're not a skaiter, I suppose?"

"No. No. Something else to think of. Good morning!"

Not another word. That was their meeting, their conversation, and their parting.

Scrooge was at first inclined to be surprised that the Spirit should attach importance to conversations apparently so trivial; but feeling assured that they must have some hidden purpose, he set himself to consider what it was likely to be. They could scarcely be supposed to have any bearing on the death of Jacob, his old partner, for that was Past, and this Ghost's province was the Future. Nor could he think of any one immediately connected with himself, to whom he could apply them. But nothing doubting that to whomsoever they applied they had some latent moral for his own improvement, he resolved to treasure up every word he heard, and everything he saw; and especially to observe the shadow of himself when it appeared. For he had an expectation that the conduct of his future self would give him the clue he missed, and would render the solution of these riddles easy.

He looked about in that very place for his own image; but another man stood in his accustomed corner, and though the clock pointed to his usual time of day for being there, he saw no likeness of himself among the multitudes that poured in through the Porch. It gave him little surprise, however; for he had been revolving in his mind a change of life, and thought and hoped he saw his new-born resolutions carried out in this.

Quiet and dark, beside him stood the Phantom, with its outstretched hand. When he roused himself from his thoughtful quest, he fancied from the turn of the hand, and its situation in reference to himself, that the Unseen Eyes were looking at him keenly. It made him shudder, and feel very cold.

They left the busy scene, and went into an obscure part of the town, where Scrooge had never penetrated before although he recognised its situation, and its bad repute. The ways were foul and narrow; the shops and houses wretched; the people half-naked, drunken, slipshod, ugly. Alleys and archways, like so many cesspools, disgorged their offences of smell, and dirt, and life, upon the straggling streets; and the whole quarter reeked with crime, with filth, and misery.

Far in this den of infamous resort, there was a low-browed, beetling shop, below a pent-house roof, where iron, old rags, bottles, bones, and greasy offal, were bought. Upon the floor within, were piled up heaps of rusty keys, nails, chains, hinges, files, scales, weights, and refuse iron of all kinds. Secrets that few would like to scrutinise were bred and hidden in mountains of unseemly rags, masses of corrupted fat, and sepulchres of bones. Sitting in among the wares he dealt in, by a charcoal-stove, made of old bricks, was a gray-haired rascal, nearly seventy years of age; who had screened himself from the cold air without, by a frousy curtaining of miscellaneous tatters, hung upon a line; and smoked his pipe in all the luxury of calm retirement.

Scrooge and the Phantom came into the presence of this man, just as a woman with a heavy bundle slunk into the shop. But she had scarcely entered, when another woman, similarly laden, came in too; and she was closely followed by a man in faded black, who was no less startled by the sight of them, than they had been upon the recognition of each other. After a short period of blank astonishment, in which the old man with the pipe had joined them, they all three burst into a laugh.

"Let the charwoman alone to be the first!" cried she who had entered first. "Let the laundress alone to be the second; and let the undertaker's man alone to be the third. Look here, old Joe, here's a chance! If we haven't all three met here without meaning it."

"You couldn't have met in a better place," said old Joe, removing his pipe from his mouth. "Come into the parlour. You were made free of it long ago, you know; and the other two an't strangers. Stop till I shut the door of the shop. Ah! How it skreeks! There an't such a rusty bit of metal in the place as its own hinges, I believe; and I'm sure there's no such old bones here, as mine. Ha, ha! We're all suitable to our calling, we're well matched. Come into the parlour. Come into the parlour."

The parlour was the space behind the screen of rags. The old man raked the fire together with an old stair-rod, and having trimmed his smoky lamp (for it was night), with the stem of his pipe, put it in his mouth again.

While he did this, the woman who had already spoken threw her bundle on the floor and sat down in a flaunting manner, on a stool, crossing her elbows on her knees, and looking with a bold defiance at the other two.

"What odds then! What odds, Mrs. Dilber?" said the woman. "Every person has a right to take care of themselves. *He* always did!"

"That's true, indeed!" said the laundress. "No man more so."

"Why then, don't stand staring as if you was afraid, woman; who's the wiser? We're not going to pick holes in each other's coats, I suppose?"

"No, indeed," said Mrs. Dilber and the man together. "We should hope not."

"Very well, then!" cried the woman. "That's enough. Who's the worse for the loss of a few things like these? Not a dead man, I suppose."

"No, indeed," said Mrs. Dilber, laughing.

"If he wanted to keep 'em after he was dead, a wicked old screw," pursued the woman, "why wasn't he natural in his lifetime? If he had been, he'd have had somebody to look after him when he was struck with Death, instead of lying gasping out his last there, alone by himself."

"It's the truest word that ever was spoke," said Mrs. Dilber. "It's a judgment on him."

"I wish it was a little heavier one," replied the woman; "and it should have been, you may depend upon it, if I could have laid my hands on anything else. Open that bundle, old Joe, and let me know the value of it. Speak out plain. I'm not afraid to be the first, nor afraid for them to see it. We knew pretty well that we were helping ourselves, before we met here, I believe. It's no sin. Open the bundle, Joe."

But the gallantry of her friends would not allow

of this; and the man in faded black, mounting the breach first, produced *his* plunder. It was not extensive. A seal or two, a pencil-case, a pair of sleeve-buttons, and a brooch of no great value, were all. They were severally examined and appraised by old Joe, who chalked the sums he was disposed to give for each, upon the wall, and added them up into a total when he found there was nothing more to come.

"That's your account," said Joe, "and I wouldn't give another sixpence, if I was to be boiled for not doing it. Who's next?"

Mrs. Dilber was next. Sheets and towels, a little wearing apparel, two old-fashioned silver teaspoons, a pair of sugar-tongs, and a few boots. Her account was stated on the wall in the same manner.

"I always give too much to ladies. It's a weakness of mine, and that's the way I ruin myself," said old Joe. "That's your account. If you asked me for another penny, and made it an open question, I'd repent of being so liberal and knock off half-a-crown."

"And now undo *my* bundle, Joe," said the first woman.

Joe went down on his knees for the greater convenience of opening it, and having unfastened a great many knots, dragged out a large and heavy roll of some dark stuff.

"What do you call this?" said Joe. "Bed-curtains!"

"Ah!" returned the woman, laughing and leaning forward on her crossed arms. "Bed-curtains!"

"You don't mean to say you took 'em down, rings and all, with him lying there?" said Joe.

"Yes I do," replied the woman. "Why not?"

"You were born to make your fortune," said Joe, "and you'll certainly do it."

"I certainly shan't hold my hand, when I get anything in it by reaching it out, for the sake of such a man as He was, I promise you, Joe," returned the woman coolly. "Don't drop that oil upon the blankets, now."

"His blankets?" asked Joe.

"Whose else's do you think?" replied the woman. "He isn't likely to take cold without 'em, I dare say."

"I hope he didn't die of anything catching? Eh?" said old Joe, stopping in his work, and looking up.

"Don't you be afraid of that," returned the woman. "I an't so fond of his company that I'd loiter about him for such things, if he did. Ah! you may look through that shirt till your eyes ache; but you won't find a hole in it, nor a threadbare place. It's the best he had, and a fine one too. They'd have wasted it, if it hadn't been for me."

"What do you call wasting of it?" asked old Joe.

"Putting it on him to be buried in, to be sure," replied the woman with a laugh. "Somebody was fool enough to do it, but I took it off again. If calico an't good enough for such a purpose, it isn't good enough for anything. It's quite as becoming to the body. He can't look uglier than he did in that one."

Scrooge listened to this dialogue in horror. As they sat grouped about their spoil, in the scanty light afforded by the old man's lamp, he viewed them with a detestation and disgust, which could hardly have been greater, though they had been obscene demons, marketing the corpse itself.

"Ha, ha!" laughed the same woman, when old Joe, producing a flannel bag with money in it, told out their several gains upon the ground. "This is the end of it, you see! He frightened every one away from him when he was alive, to profit us when he was dead! Ha, ha, ha!"

"Spirit!" said Scrooge, shuddering from head to foot. "I see, I see. The case of this unhappy man might be my own. My life tends that way, now. Merciful Heaven, what is this!"

He recoiled in terror, for the scene had changed, and now he almost touched a bed: a bare, uncurtained bed: on which, beneath a ragged sheet, there lay a something covered up, which, though it was dumb, announced itself in awful language.

The room was very dark, too dark to be observed with any accuracy, though Scrooge glanced round it in obedience to a secret impulse, anxious to know what kind of room it was. A pale light, rising in the outer air, fell straight upon the bed; and on it, plundered and bereft, unwatched, unwept, uncared for, was the body of this man.

Scrooge glanced towards the Phantom. Its steady hand was pointed to the head. The cover was so carelessly adjusted that the slightest raising of it, the motion of a finger upon Scrooge's part, would have disclosed the face. He thought of it, felt how easy it would be to do, and longed to do it; but had no more power to withdraw the veil than to dismiss the spectre at his side.

Oh, cold, cold, rigid, dreadful Death, set up thine altar here, and dress it with such terrors as thou hast at thy command: for this is thy dominion! But of the loved, revered, and honoured head, thou canst not turn one hair to thy dread purposes, or make one feature odious. It is not that the hand is heavy and will fall down when released; it is not that the heart and pulse are still; but that the hand WAS open, generous, and true; the heart brave, warm, and tender; and the pulse a man's. Strike, Shadow, strike! And see his good deeds springing from the wound, to sow the world with life immortal!

No voice pronounced these words in Scrooge's ears, and yet he heard them when he looked upon the bed. He thought, if this man could be raised up now, what would be his foremost thoughts? Avarice, hard dealing, griping cares? They have brought him to a rich end, truly!

He lay, in the dark empty house, with not a man, a woman, or a child, to say that he was kind to me in this or that, and for the memory of one kind word I will be kind to him. A cat was tearing at the door, and there was a sound of gnawing rats beneath the hearth-stone. What *they* wanted in the room of death, and why they were so restless and disturbed, Scrooge did not dare to think.

"Spirit!" he said, "this is a fearful place. In leaving it, I shall not leave its lesson, trust me. Let us go!"

Still the Ghost pointed with an unmoved finger to the head.

"I understand you," Scrooge returned, "and I would do it, if I could. But I have not the power, Spirit. I have not the power."

Again it seemed to look upon him.

"If there is any person in the town, who feels emotion caused by this man's death," said Scrooge quite agonised, "show that person to me, Spirit, I beseech you!"

The Phantom spread its dark robe before him for a moment, like a wing; and withdrawing it, revealed a room by daylight, where a mother and her children were.

She was expecting some one, and with anxious

eagerness; for she walked up and down the room; started at every sound; looked out from the window; glanced at the clock; tried, but in vain, to work with her needle; and could hardly bear the voices of the children in their play.

At length the long-expected knock was heard. She hurried to the door, and met her husband; a man whose face was care-worn and depressed, though he was young. There was a remarkable expression in it now; a kind of serious delight of which he felt ashamed, and which he struggled to repress.

He sat down to the dinner that had been hoarding for him by the fire; and when she asked him faintly what news (which was not until after a long silence), he appeared embarrassed how to answer.

"Is it good," she said, "or bad?"–to help him.

"Bad," he answered.

"We are quite ruined?"

"No. There is hope yet, Caroline."

"If *he* relents," she said, amazed, "there is! Nothing is past hope, if such a miracle has happened."

"He is past relenting," said her husband. "He is dead."

She was a mild and patient creature if her face spoke truth; but she was thankful in her soul to hear it, and she said so, with clasped hands. She prayed forgiveness the next moment, and was sorry; but the first was the emotion of her heart.

"What the half-drunken woman whom I told you of last night, said to me, when I tried to see him and obtain a week's delay; and what I thought was a mere excuse to avoid me; turns out to have been quite true. He was not only very ill, but dying then."

"To whom will our debt be transferred?"

"I don't know. But before that time we shall be ready with the money; and even though we were not, it would be bad fortune indeed to find so merciless a creditor in his successor. We may sleep to-night with light hearts, Caroline!"

Yes. Soften it as they would, their hearts were lighter. The children's faces, hushed and clustered round to hear what they so little understood, were brighter; and it was a happier house for this man's death! The only emotion that the Ghost could show him, caused by the event, was one of pleasure.

"Let me see some tenderness connected with a death," said Scrooge, "or that dark chamber, Spirit, which we left just now, will be for ever present to me."

The Ghost conducted him through several streets familiar to his feet; and as they went along, Scrooge looked here and there to find himself, but nowhere was he to be seen. They entered poor Bob Cratchit's house; the dwelling he had visited before; and found the mother and the children seated round the fire.

Quiet. Very quiet. The noisy little Cratchits were as still as statues in one corner, and sat looking up at Peter, who had a book before him. The mother and her daughters were engaged in sewing. But surely they were very quiet!

"'And He took a child, and set him in the midst of them.'"

Where had Scrooge heard those words? He had not dreamed them. The boy must have read them out, as he and the Spirit crossed the threshold. Why did he not go on?

The mother laid her work upon the table, and put her hand up to her face.

"The colour hurts my eyes," she said.

The colour? Ah, poor Tiny Tim!

"They're better now again," said Cratchit's wife. "It makes them weak by candle-light; and I wouldn't show weak eyes to your father when he comes home, for the world. It must be near his time."

"Past it rather," Peter answered, shutting up his book. "But I think he's walked a little slower than he used, these few last evenings, mother."

They were very quiet again. At last she said, and in a steady, cheerful voice, that only faultered once:

"I have known him walk with–I have known him walk with Tiny Tim upon his shoulder, very fast indeed."

"And so have I," cried Peter. "Often."

"And so have I!" exclaimed another. So had all.

"But he was very light to carry," she resumed, intent upon her work, "and his father loved him so, that it was no trouble–no trouble. And there is your father at the door!"

She hurried out to meet him; and little Bob in his comforter–he had need of it, poor fellow–came in. His tea was ready for him on the hob, and they all tried who should help him to it most. Then the two young Cratchits got upon his knees and laid, each child a little cheek, against his face, as if they said, "Don't mind it, father. Don't be grieved!"

Bob was very cheerful with them, and spoke pleasantly to all the family. He looked at the work upon the table, and praised the industry and speed of Mrs. Cratchit and the girls. They would be done long before Sunday, he said.

"Sunday! You went to-day then, Robert?" said his wife.

"Yes, my dear," returned Bob. "I wish you could have gone. It would have done you good to see how green a place it is. But you'll see it often. I promised him that I would walk there on a Sunday. My little, little child!" cried Bob. "My little child!"

He broke down all at once. He couldn't help it. If he could have helped it, he and his child would have been farther apart perhaps than they were.

He left the room, and went up stairs into the room above, which was lighted cheerfully, and hung with Christmas. There was a chair set close beside the child, and there were signs of some one having been there, lately. Poor Bob sat down in it, and when he had thought a little and composed himself, he kissed the little face. He was reconciled to what had happened, and went down again quite happy.

They drew about the fire, and talked; the girls and mother working still. Bob told them of the extraordinary kindness of Mr. Scrooge's nephew, whom he had scarcely seen but once, and who, meeting him in the street that day, and seeing that he looked a little–"just a little down you know" said Bob, inquired what had happened to distress him. "On which," said Bob, "for he is the pleasantest-spoken gentleman you ever heard, I told him. 'I am heartily sorry for it, Mr. Cratchit,' he said, 'and heartily sorry for your good wife.' By the bye, how he ever knew *that,* I don't know."

"Knew what, my dear."

"Why, that you were a good wife," replied Bob.

"Everybody knows that!" said Peter.

"Very well observed, my boy!" cried Bob. "I hope they do. 'Heartily sorry,' he said, 'for your good wife. If I can be of any service to you in any way,' he said, giving me his card, 'that's where I live. Pray come to me.' Now, it wasn't," cried Bob, "for the sake of anything he might be able to do for us, so much as for his kind way, that this was quite delightful. It really seemed as if he had known our Tiny Tim, and felt with us."

"I'm sure he's a good soul!" said Mrs. Cratchit.

"You would be surer of it, my dear," returned Bob, "if you saw and spoke to him. I shouldn't be at all surprised, mark what I say, if he got Peter a better situation."

"Only hear that, Peter," said Mrs. Cratchit.

"And then," cried one of the girls, "Peter will be keeping company with some one, and setting up for himself."

"Get along with you!" retorted Peter, grinning.

"It's just as likely as not," said Bob, "one of these days; though there's plenty of time for that, my dear. But however and whenever we part from one another, I am sure we shall none of us forget poor Tiny Tim–shall we–or this first parting that there was among us?"

"Never, father!" cried they all.

"And I know," said Bob, "I know, my dears, that when we recollect how patient and how mild he was; although he was a little, little child; we shall not quarrel easily among ourselves, and forget poor Tiny Tim in doing it."

"No, never, father!" they all cried again.

"I am very happy," said little Bob, "I am very happy!"

Mrs. Cratchit kissed him, his daughters kissed him, the two young Cratchits kissed him, and Peter and himself shook hands. Spirit of Tiny Tim, thy childish essence was from God!

"Spectre," said Scrooge, "something informs me that our parting moment is at hand. I know it, but I know not how. Tell me what man that was whom we saw lying dead?"

The Ghost of Christmas Yet To Come conveyed him, as before–though at a different time, he thought: indeed, there seemed no order in these latter visions, save that they were in the Future–into the resorts of business men, but showed him not himself. Indeed, the Spirit did not stay for anything, but went straight on, as to the end just now desired, until besought by Scrooge to tarry for a moment.

"This court," said Scrooge, "through which we hurry now, is where my place of occupation is, and has been for a length of time. I see the house. Let me behold what I shall be, in days to come."

The Spirit stopped; the hand was pointed elsewhere.

"The house is yonder," Scrooge exclaimed. "Why do you point away?"

The inexorable finger underwent no change.

Scrooge hastened to the window of his office, and looked in. It was an office still, but not his. The furniture was not the same, and the figure in the chair was not himself. The Phantom pointed as before.

He joined it once again, and wondering why and whither he had gone, accompanied it until they reached an iron gate. He paused to look round before entering.

A churchyard. Here, then, the wretched man whose name he had now to learn, lay underneath the ground. It was a worthy place. Walled in by houses; overrun by grass and weeds, the growth of vegetation's death, not life; choked up with too much burying; fat with repleted appetite. A worthy place!

The Spirit stood among the graves, and pointed down to One. He advanced towards it trembling. The Phantom was exactly as it had been, but he dreaded that he saw new meaning in its solemn shape.

"Before I draw nearer to that stone to which you point," said Scrooge, "answer me one question. Are these the shadows of the things that Will be, or are they shadows of things that May be, only?"

Still the Ghost pointed downward to the grave by which it stood.

"Men's courses will foreshadow certain ends, to which, if persevered in, they must lead," said Scrooge. "But if the courses be departed from, the ends will change. Say it is thus with what you show me!"

The Spirit was immovable as ever.

Scrooge crept towards it, trembling as he went; and following the finger, read upon the stone of the neglected grave his own name, EBENEZER SCROOGE.

"Am *I* that man who lay upon the bed?" he cried, upon his knees.

The finger pointed from the grave to him, and back again.

"No, Spirit! Oh, no, no!"

The finger still was there.

"Spirit!" he cried, tight clutching at its robe, "hear me! I am not the man I was. I will not be the man I must have been but for this intercourse. Why show me this, if I am past all hope?"

For the first time the hand appeared to shake.

"Good Spirit," he pursued, as down upon the ground he fell before it: "Your nature intercedes for me, and pities me. Assure me that I yet may change these shadows you have shown me, by an altered life!"

The kind hand trembled.

"I will honour Christmas in my heart, and try to keep it all the year. I will live in the Past, the Present, and the Future. The Spirits of all Three shall strive within me. I will not shut out the lessons that they teach. Oh, tell me I may sponge away the writing on this stone!"

In his agony, he caught the spectral hand. It sought to free itself, but he was strong in his entreaty, and detained it. The Spirit, stronger yet, repulsed him.

Holding up his hands in a last prayer to have his fate reversed, he saw an alteration in the Phantom's hood and dress. It shrunk, collapsed, and dwindled down into a bedpost.

Stave  The End of It

Yes! and the bedpost was his own. The bed was his own, the room was his own. Best and happiest of all, the Time before him was his own, to make amends in!

"I will live in the Past, the Present, and the Future!" Scrooge repeated, as he scrambled out of bed. "The Spirits of all Three shall strive within me. Oh Jacob Marley! Heaven, and the Christmas Time be praised for this! I say it on my knees, old Jacob; on my knees!"

He was so fluttered and so glowing with his good intentions, that his broken voice would scarcely answer to his call. He had been sobbing violently in his conflict with the Spirit, and his face was wet with tears.

"They are not torn down," cried Scrooge, folding one of his bed-curtains in his arms, "they are not torn down, rings and all. They are here: I am here: the shadows of the things that would have been, may be dispelled. They will be. I know they will!"

His hands were busy with his garments all this time: turning them inside out, putting them on upside down, tearing them, mislaying them, making them parties to every kind of extravagance.

"I don't know what to do!" cried Scrooge, laughing and crying in the same breath; and making a perfect Laocoön of himself with his stockings. "I am as light as a feather, I am as happy as an angel, I am as merry as a school-boy. I am as giddy as a drunken man. A merry Christmas to everybody! A happy New Year to all the world! Hallo here! Whoop! Hallo!"

He had frisked into the sitting-room, and was now standing there: perfectly winded.

"There's the saucepan that the gruel was in!"

cried Scrooge, starting off again, and frisking round the fire-place. "There's the door, by which the Ghost of Jacob Marley entered! There's the corner where the Ghost of Christmas Present, sat! There's the window where I saw the wandering Spirits! It's all right, it's all true, it all happened. Ha ha ha!"

Really, for a man who had been out of practice for so many years, it was a splendid laugh, a most illustrious laugh. The father of a long, long line of brilliant laughs!

"I don't know what day of the month it is!" said Scrooge. "I don't know how long I've been among the Spirits. I don't know anything. I'm quite a baby. Never mind. I don't care. I'd rather be a baby. Hallo! Whoop! Hallo here!"

He was checked in his transports by the churches ringing out the lustiest peals he had ever heard. Clash, clang, hammer, ding, dong, bell. Bell, dong, ding, hammer, clang, clash! Oh, glorious, glorious!

Running to the window, he opened it, and put out his head. No fog, no mist; clear, bright, jovial, stirring, cold; cold, piping for the blood to dance to; Golden sunlight; Heavenly sky; sweet fresh air; merry bells. Oh, glorious. Glorious!

"What's to-day?" cried Scrooge, calling downward to a boy in Sunday clothes, who perhaps had loitered in to look about him.

"EH?" returned the boy, with all his might of wonder.

"What's to-day, my fine fellow?" said Scrooge.

"To-day!" replied the boy. "Why, CHRISTMAS DAY."

"It's Christmas Day!" said Scrooge to himself. "I haven't missed it. The Spirits have done it all in one night. They can do anything they like. Of course they can. Of course they can. Hallo, my fine fellow!"

"Hallo!" returned the boy.

"Do you know the Poulterer's, in the next street but one, at the corner?" Scrooge inquired.

"I should hope I did," replied the lad.

"An intelligent boy!" said Scrooge. "A remarkable boy! Do you know whether they've sold the prize Turkey that was hanging up there? Not the little prize Turkey: the big one?"

"What, the one as big as me?" returned the boy.

"What a delightful boy!" said Scrooge. "It's a pleasure to talk to him. Yes, my buck!"

"It's hanging there now," replied the boy.

"Is it?" said Scrooge. "Go and buy it."

"Walk-ER!" exclaimed the boy.

"No, no," said Scrooge, "I am in earnest. Go and buy it, and tell 'em to bring it here, that I may give them the direction where to take it. Come back with the man, and I'll give you a shilling. Come back with him in less than five minutes, and I'll give you half-a-crown!"

The boy was off like a shot. He must have had a steady hand at a trigger who could have got a shot off half so fast.

"I'll send it to Bob Cratchit's!" whispered Scrooge, rubbing his hands, and splitting with a laugh. "He shan't know who sends it. It's twice the size of Tiny Tim. Joe Miller never made such a joke as sending it to Bob's will be!"

The hand in which he wrote the address was not a steady one, but write it he did, somehow, and went down stairs to open the street door, ready for the coming of the poulterer's man. As he stood there, waiting his arrival, the knocker caught his eye.

"I shall love it, as long as I live!" cried Scrooge, patting it with his hand. "I scarcely ever looked at it before. What an honest expression it has in its face! It's a wonderful knocker!–Here's the Turkey. Hallo! Whoop! How are you! Merry Christmas!"

It *was* a Turkey! He never could have stood upon his legs, that bird. He would have snapped 'em short off in a minute, like sticks of sealing-wax.

"Why, it's impossible to carry that to Camden Town," said Scrooge. "You must have a cab."

The chuckle with which he said this, and the chuckle with which he paid for the Turkey, and the chuckle with which he paid for the cab, and the chuckle with which he recompensed the boy, were only to be exceeded by the chuckle with which he sat down breathless in his chair again, and chuckled till he cried.

Shaving was not an easy task, for his hand continued to shake very much; and shaving requires attention, even when you don't dance while you are at it. But if he had cut the end of his nose off, he would have put a piece of sticking-plaister over it, and been quite satisfied.

He dressed himself "all in his best," and at last got out into the streets. The people were by this time pouring forth, as he had seen them with the Ghost of Christmas Present; and walking with his hands behind him, Scrooge regarded every one with a delightful smile. He looked so irresistibly pleasant, in a word, that three or four good-humoured fellows said, "Good morning, sir! A merry Christmas to you!" And Scrooge said often afterwards, that of all the blithe sounds he had ever heard, those were the blithest in his ears.

He had not gone far, when coming on towards him he beheld the portly gentleman, who had walked into his counting-house the day before and said, "Scrooge and Marley's, I believe?" It sent a pang across his heart to think how this old gentleman would look upon him when they met; but he knew what path lay straight before him, and he took it.

"My dear sir," said Scrooge, quickening his pace, and taking the old gentleman by both his hands. "How do you do? I hope you succeeded yesterday. It was very kind of you. A merry Christmas to you, sir!"

"Mr. Scrooge?"

"Yes," said Scrooge. "That is my name, and I fear it may not be pleasant to you. Allow me to ask your pardon. And will you have the goodness"–here Scrooge whispered in his ear.

"Lord bless me!" cried the gentleman, as if his breath were gone. "My dear Mr. Scrooge, are you serious?"

"If you please," said Scrooge. "Not a farthing less. A great many back-payments are included in it, I assure you. Will you do me that favour?"

"My dear sir," said the other, shaking hands with him. "I don't know what to say to such munifi–"

"Don't say anything, please," retorted Scrooge. "Come and see me. Will you come and see me?"

"I will!" cried the old gentleman. And it was clear he meant to do it.

"Thank'ee," said Scrooge. "I am much obliged to you. I thank you fifty times. Bless you!"

He went to church, and walked about the streets, and watched the people hurrying to and fro, and patted children on the head, and questioned beggars, and looked down into the kitchens of houses, and up to the windows; and found that everything could yield him pleasure. He had never dreamed that any walk–that anything–could give him so much happiness. In the afternoon, he turned his steps towards his nephew's house.

He passed the door a dozen times, before he had the courage to go up and knock. But he made a dash, and did it:

"Is your master at home, my dear?" said Scrooge to the girl. Nice girl! Very.

"Yes, sir."

"Where is he, my love?" said Scrooge.

"He's in the dining-room, sir, along with mistress. I'll show you up stairs, if you please."

"Thank'ee. He knows me," said Scrooge, with his hand already on the dining-room lock. "I'll go in here, my dear."

He turned it gently, and sidled his face in, round the door. They were looking at the table (which was spread out in great array); for these young housekeepers are always nervous on such points, and like to see that everything is right.

"Fred!" said Scrooge.

Dear heart alive, how his niece by marriage started! Scrooge had forgotten, for the moment, about her sitting in the corner with the footstool, or he wouldn't have done it, on any account.

"Why bless my soul!" cried Fred, "who's that?"

"It's I. Your uncle Scrooge. I have come to dinner. Will you let me in, Fred?"

Let him in! It is a mercy he didn't shake his arm off. He was at home in five minutes. Nothing could be heartier. His niece looked just the same. So did Topper when *he* came. So did the plump sister, when *she* came. So did every one when *they* came. Wonderful party, wonderful games, wonderful unanimity, won-der-ful happiness!

But he was early at the office next morning. Oh, he was early there. If he could only be there first, and catch Bob Cratchit coming late! That was the thing he had set his heart upon.

And he did it; yes, he did! The clock struck nine. No Bob. A quarter past. No Bob. He was full eighteen minutes and a half, behind his time. Scrooge sat with his door wide open, that he might see him come into the Tank.

His hat was off, before he opened the door; his comforter too. He was on his stool in a jiffy; driving away with his pen, as if he were trying to overtake nine o'clock.

"Hallo!" growled Scrooge, in his accustomed voice as near as he could feign it. "What do you mean by coming here at this time of day?"

"I am very sorry, sir." said Bob. "I *am* behind my time."

"You are." repeated Scrooge, "Yes. I think you are. Step this way, if you please."

"It's only once a year, sir," pleaded Bob, appearing from the Tank. "It shall not be repeated. I was making rather merry yesterday, sir."

"Now, I'll tell you what, my friend," said Scrooge, "I am not going to stand this sort of thing any longer. And therefore," he continued, leaping from his stool, and giving Bob such a dig in the waistcoat that he staggered back into the Tank again: "and therefore I am about to raise your salary!"

Bob trembled, and got a little nearer to the ruler. He had a momentary idea of knocking Scrooge down with it; holding him; and calling to the people in the court for help and a strait-waistcoat.

"A merry Christmas, Bob!" said Scrooge, with an earnestness that could not be mistaken, as he clapped him on the back. "A merrier Christmas, Bob, my good fellow, than I have given you, for many a year! I'll raise your salary, and endeavour to assist your struggling family, and we will discuss your affairs this very afternoon, over a Christmas bowl of smoking bishop, Bob! Make up the fires, and buy another coal-scuttle before you dot another i, Bob Cratchit!"

Scrooge was better than his word. He did it all, and infinitely more; and to Tiny Tim, who did *not* die, he was a second father. He became as good a friend, as good a master, and as good a man, as the good old city knew, or any other good old city, town, or borough, in the good old world. Some people laughed to see the alteration in him, but he let them laugh, and little heeded them; for he was wise enough to know that nothing ever happened on this globe, for good, at which some people did not have their fill of laughter in the outset; and knowing that such as these would be blind anyway, he thought it quite as well that they should wrinkle up their eyes in grins, as have the malady in less attractive forms. His own heart laughed: and that was quite enough for him.

He had no further intercourse with Spirits, but lived upon the Total Abstinence Principle, ever afterwards; and it was always said of him, that he knew how to keep Christmas well, if any man alive possessed the knowledge. May that be truly said of us, and all of us! And so, as Tiny Tim observed, God bless Us, Every One!

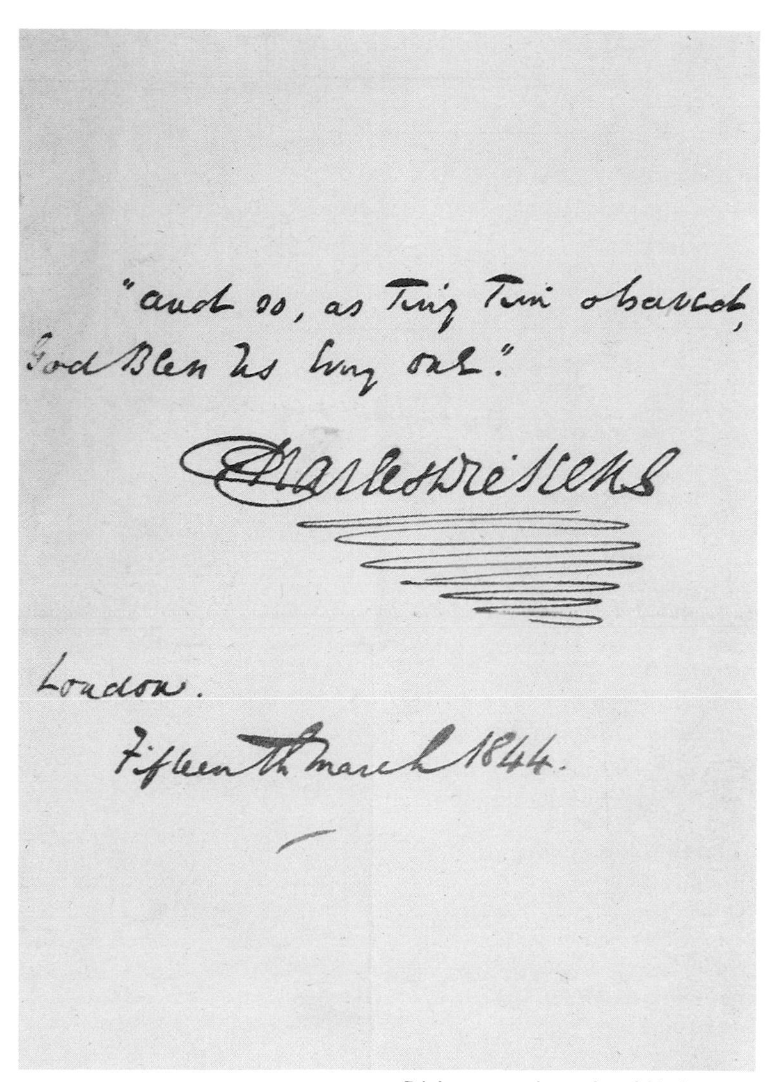
"and so, as Tiny Tim observed, God Bless Us Every One."

Charles Dickens

London.

Fifteenth March 1844.

Dickens sometimes closed his letters (or autographs) with Tiny Tim's "God bless us, every one!" By permission of The Pierpont Morgan Library, New York.

The End

Acknowledgements

This book was designed by
Rudolph de Harak,
Frank Benedict
and Ellen Lupton,
Rudolph de Harak
& Associates, Inc.,
New York, New York.

The text was written by
Tim Hallinan
and researched by
Munyin Choy,
Stone Hallinan Associates, Inc.,
Los Angeles, California.

The photographs were taken by
David James
on location in Shrewsbury, England
during the filming of
A Christmas Carol,
in March and April, 1984.

The film *A Christmas Carol*
was produced by
Entertainment Partners, Inc.,
New York, New York;
Robert E. Fuisz,
Executive Producer,
William F. Storke and
Alfred R. Kelman,
Producers.

The volume was printed by
Case-Hoyt Color Printers,
Rochester, New York.

The illustrations were provided by:

Arthur Rackham Collection, Rare
Book and Manuscript Library,
Columbia University

Beinecke Rare Book and Manuscript Library, Yale University

Dickens House Museum, London

Forster Collection, Victoria and
Albert Museum, London

Houghton Library, Harvard
University

New York Public Library, Astor,
Lenox and Tilden Foundations

New York Public Library Picture
Collection

The Pierpont Morgan Library,
New York

The Royal Holloway College,
University of London

Dr. Frank Tassone, The Dickens
Fellowship, New York

Special thanks to the Archives of
Hallmark Cards, Inc., Kansas
City, Missouri.

William Caslon IV (1781-1869) was Dickens' contemporary and countryman. He came from four generations of English typographers and printers and designed type faces for fine printing and the growing mass publishing industry.

The book was set in Caslon 540
by Typologic Inc.,
New York, New York.